NCFE

Level 1/2 Technical Award

HEALTH AND FITNESS

Ross Howitt
Mike Murray

HODDER
EDUCATION
AN HACHETTE UK COMPANY

Although every effort has been made to ensure that website addresses are correct at time of going to press, Hodder Education cannot be held responsible for the content of any website mentioned in this book. It is sometimes possible to find a relocated web page by typing in the address of the home page for a website in the URL window of your browser.

Hachette UK's policy is to use papers that are natural, renewable and recyclable products and made from wood grown in sustainable forests. The logging and manufacturing processes are expected to conform to the environmental regulations of the country of origin.

Orders: please contact Bookpoint Ltd, 130 Park Drive, Milton Park, Abingdon, Oxon OX14 4SE. Telephone: +44 (0)1235 827827. Fax: +44 (0)1235 400401. Email education@bookpoint.co.uk Lines are open from 9 a.m. to 5 p.m., Monday to Saturday, with a 24-hour message answering service. You can also order through our website: www.hoddereducation.co.uk

ISBN: 978 1 5104 4640 3

First published in 2018 by
Hodder Education,
An Hachette UK Company
Carmelite House
50 Victoria Embankment
London EC4Y 0DZ

www.hoddereducation.co.uk

Impression number   10 9 8 7 6 5 4 3 2

Year   2022 2021 2020 2019

Cover photo © lassedesignen – stock.adobe.com

Illustrations by Barking Dog Art

Typeset in India.

Printed in Italy.

A catalogue record for this title is available from the British Library.

Contents

How to use this book   iv

Introduction to NCFE Level 1/2 Technical Award in Health and Fitness   v

Acknowledgements   vi

Unit 1 Introduction to body systems and principles of training in health and fitness   1

Learning outcome 1: understand the structure and function of body systems and how they apply to health and fitness   2

Learning outcome 2: understand the effects of health and fitness activities on the body   56

Learning outcome 3: understand health and fitness and the components of fitness   62

Learning outcome 4: understand the principles of training   70

Unit 2 Preparing and planning for health and fitness   75

Learning outcome 1: understand the impact of lifestyle on health and fitness   76

Learning outcome 2: understand how to test and develop components of fitness   90

Learning outcome 3: understand how to apply health and fitness analyses and set goals   112

Learning outcome 4: understand the structure of a health and fitness programme and how to prepare safely   118

Glossary   133

Unit 1 answers   138

Unit 2 answers   145

Index   150

How to use this book

This book is designed to help you develop the knowledge, understanding and practical skills you will need during the NCFE Level 1/2 Technical Award in Health and Fitness course.

A range of different features appear throughout the book to support your learning.

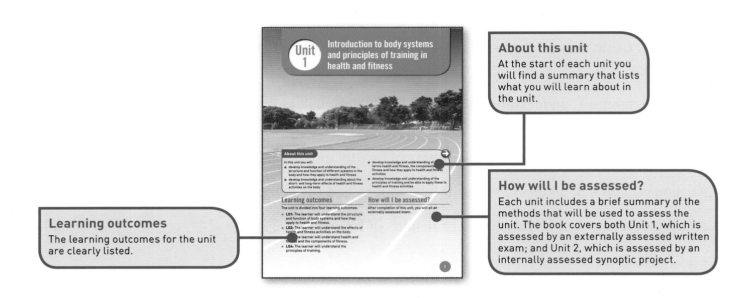

About this unit
At the start of each unit you will find a summary that lists what you will learn about in the unit.

How will I be assessed?
Each unit includes a brief summary of the methods that will be used to assess the unit. The book covers both Unit 1, which is assessed by an externally assessed written exam; and Unit 2, which is assessed by an internally assessed synoptic project.

Learning outcomes
The learning outcomes for the unit are clearly listed.

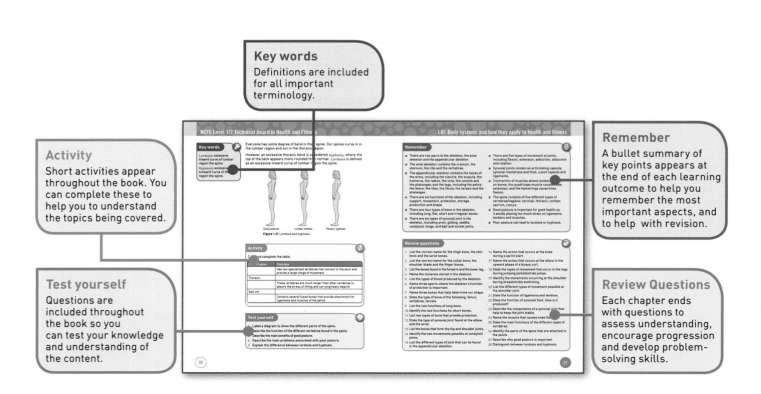

Key words
Definitions are included for all important terminology.

Activity
Short activities appear throughout the book. You can complete these to help you to understand the topics being covered.

Test yourself
Questions are included throughout the book so you can test your knowledge and understanding of the content.

Remember
A bullet summary of key points appears at the end of each learning outcome to help you remember the most important aspects, and to help with revision.

Review Questions
Each chapter ends with questions to assess understanding, encourage progression and develop problem-solving skills.

Introduction to NCFE Level 1/2 Technical Award in Health and Fitness

This book has been written to help you to master the skills, knowledge and understanding you need for the NCFE Level 1/2 Technical Award in Health and Fitness.

Throughout the course you will learn how to:

- understand and identify the main body systems and their functions
- understand the principles of training and FITT
- explore how physical activities affect the body in the short- and long-term
- use relevant fitness tests for specific health and skill components of fitness
- understand different lifestyle analysis tools and apply them
- create a health and fitness programme.

You will develop your practical skills and learn how to evaluate your own work, adapt your ideas and respond to feedback.

The book is divided into two units:

Unit 01 Introduction to body systems and principles of training in health and fitness

In this unit, you will learn about the structure and function of key body systems. You will know and understand the short- and long-term effects that health and fitness activities can have on the body. You will also learn about the components of fitness and the principles of training.

Unit 02 Preparing and planning for health and fitness

This unit looks at how to prepare and plan for health and fitness. You will learn about the impact of lifestyle on health and fitness. You will learn how to apply health and fitness analyses to set goals, and how to test and develop components of fitness. You will also learn how to structure a health and fitness programme and prepare safely for activities.

Summary of assessment

The table below summarises how you will be assessed for NCFE Level 1/2 Technical Award in Health and Fitness.

Component	Assessment type	Time	% of qualification
Unit 01 Introduction to body systems and principles of training in health and fitness	Written examination	1 hour 30 minutes	40%
Unit 02 Preparing and planning for health and fitness	Synoptic project	Approx. 22 hours	60%

Acknowledgements

The Publishers would like to thank the following for permission to reproduce copyright material.

Photo on p.1 © kunchainub/stock.adobe.com; Fig.1.60 © JGI/Jamie Grill/Blend Images/Alamy Stock Photo; Fig.1.61 © Dotshock/123RF; Fig.1.62 © istockphotoluis/iStock/Thinkstock; Fig.1.63 © Viafilms/iStock/Thinkstock; Fig.1.64 © BananaStock/Thinkstock; Fig.1.65 © Wavebreakmedia Ltd/Thinkstock; Fig.1.68 © pixelrain/stock.adobe.com; Fig.1.69 © Tom King/Alamy Stock Photo; Fig.1.70 © Mariano Pozo Ruiz/Fotolia; photo on p.75 © Videowokart/stock.adobe.com; Fig.2.3 and p.82 contain public sector information licensed under the Open Government Licence v3.0; Fig.2.4 © kkong/Alamy Stock Photo; Fig.2.5 © Huseyin Onur Cicekci/iStock/Thinkstock; Fig.2.7 © Marcin/Sylwia C./Fotolia.com; Fig.2.9 © Sputnik/TopFoto.co.uk; Tables 2.4, 2.5, 2.6, 2.7, 2.8, 2.12 and 2.13 from Top End Sports, www.topendsports.com; Fig.2.14 © xalanx/stock.adobe.com; Fig.2.17 ©lunamarina/stock.adobe.com; Fig.2.18 © WavebreakMediaMicro/stock.adobe.com; Fig.2.19 © Daxiao Productions/stock.adobe.com; Fig.2.20 © nd3000/stock.adobe.com; Fig.2.21 © gstockstudio/stock.adobe.com; Fig.2.22 © WavebreakMediaMicro/stock.adobe.com; Fig.2.23 top © Thomas Northcut/Photodisc/Thinkstock, bottom left © Kikovic/iStock/Thinkstock, right © monkeybusinessimages/iStock/Thinkstock; Fig.2.25 © Ivan Kruk/stock.adobe.com; Fig.2.26 © designer491/stock.adobe.com; Fig.2.27 © WavebreakMediaMicro/stock.adobe.com; Fig.2.28 © patpitchaya/stock.adobe.com; Fig.2.32 © ruigsantos/stock.adobe.com; Fig.2.33 © Nicholas Piccillo/stock.adobe.com; Fig.2.34 with permission from Breaking Muscle, www.breakingmuscle.com; Fig.2.35 © zeljkomatic76/stock.adobe.com; Fig.2.36 © .shock/stock.adobe.com; Fig.2.37 © Jale Ibrak/stock.adobe.com; Fig.2.38 © Sandor Jackal/Fotolia; Fig.2.39 © Ruslan Ivantsov/stock.adobe.com; Fig.2.40 © xalanx/stock.adobe.com.

Every effort has been made to trace all copyright holders, but if any have been inadvertently overlooked, the Publishers will be pleased to make the necessary arrangements at the first opportunity.

Unit 1

Introduction to body systems and principles of training in health and fitness

About this unit

In this unit you will:

- develop knowledge and understanding of the structure and function of different systems in the body and how they apply to health and fitness
- develop knowledge and understanding about the short- and long-term effects of health and fitness activities on the body

- develop knowledge and understanding of the terms health and fitness, the components of fitness and how they apply to health and fitness activities
- develop knowledge and understanding of the principles of training and be able to apply these to health and fitness activities.

Learning outcomes

The unit is divided into four learning outcomes:

- **LO1:** The learner will understand the structure and function of body systems and how they apply to health and fitness.
- **LO2:** The learner will understand the effects of health and fitness activities on the body.
- **LO3:** The learner will understand health and fitness and the components of fitness.
- **LO4:** The learner will understand the principles of training.

How will I be assessed?

After completion of this unit, you will sit an externally assessed exam.

Learning outcome 1: understand the structure and function of body systems and how they apply to health and fitness

In this learning outcome you will be shown:

- that the skeleton is divided into two sections and the location of named bones
- the functions of the skeletal system
- the types of bone in the body, their primary function and how they relate to movement, with examples of each type of bone
- the types of joints in the body, with examples of each type of joint, and how ball and socket and hinge joints link to joint actions
- different types of movement, how they relate to ball and socket and hinge joints and their application to specific actions in health and fitness
- the location of different structures within the knee joint, and what their functions are
- that the spine is divided into regions and the location of each region
- the importance of posture when performing health and fitness activities
- the different types of muscle, where they are located, their characteristics and functions
- the location of the main muscles of the muscular system

- how muscles work in antagonistic pairs to produce movement at a joint and how to apply this principle to specific actions in health and fitness
- the different types of muscle contractions and apply these to specific actions and muscles
- the different muscle fibre types and their characteristics (colour, contraction speed and fatigue speed), and which health and fitness activities each type is suited to
- that individuals have differing numbers of Type 1 and Type 2 muscle fibres and that specific training can affect the performance of muscle fibre types
- the pathway of air through the respiratory system
- the mechanics of breathing
- the lung volumes and the changes that happen in these volumes from rest to participating in health and fitness activities
- the structure of blood vessels and how that structure relates to the functions of blood distribution
- that the blood vessels redistribute blood (vascular shunt) during health and fitness activities
- that the heart is divided into two sides (left and right) and the location of structures within the heart
- the order of the cardiac cycle and the pathway of oxygenated and deoxygenated blood around the heart
- cardiovascular measurements, including how they are relevant to health and fitness and how to of them are measured
- the two different types of blood pressure and the range of blood pressure classification
- the aerobic and anaerobic energy systems and how to apply these to health and fitness activities.

1.1 Skeletal system

1.1.1 Structure of the skeleton

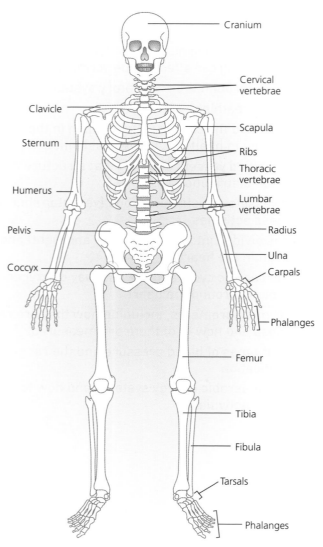

Figure 1.1 The skeleton

The skeleton is the framework of the body. Your skeleton is made up of bones, and is divided into two sections, the **axial** and the **appendicular skeleton**.

The axial skeleton is the central core of our skeleton.

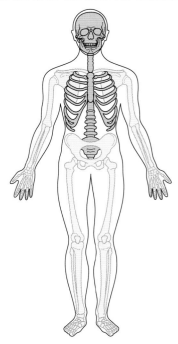

Figure 1.2 The axial skeleton

The axial skeleton contains the bones of the head, the **cranium**, and the bones in the chest. The bones in the chest include the **ribs**, the **sternum** (sometimes called the breast bone), and the **vertebrae** (sometimes called the backbone).

The appendicular skeleton forms the arms and legs.

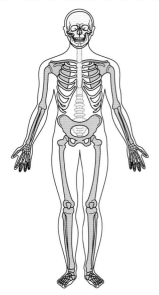

Figure 1.3 The appendicular skeleton

The arms are attached to the axial skeleton by the **clavicle** (sometimes called the collar bone), and **scapula** (sometimes called the shoulder blade).

Activity

Write the names of the bones in the arms on sticky labels and attach them to your body in the correct place. Repeat this idea with the bones in the legs.

The bones of the arm include the **humerus** in the upper arm, the **radius** and **ulna** in the forearm and the **carpals** found in the wrist. The bones in the fingers are called **phalanges**.

The legs are attached to the axial skeleton by the **pelvis**. The bone in the thigh is called the **femur**. The bones in the lower leg include the **tibia** and the **fibula**. The bones in the foot are the **tarsals** and the toes are made up of **phalanges**.

Activity

Use the internet (www.tinyurl.com/y9j9wey3) to find and print an image of the skeleton. Use different coloured pens to colour in the axial and appendicular skeletons.

Test yourself

1 Name the four bones in the axial skeleton.
2 Name all the bones found in the arm.
3 Name all the bones found in the leg.
4 Name the bones found in the hands and feet.

Activity

Use the internet (www.tinyurl.com/y9j9wey3) to find and print an image of the skeleton. Name as many bones as you can by writing their names on the image.

1.1.2 Functions of the skeletal system

The functions of the skeleton include:

1 **Support** – bones are solid and rigid; they keep us upright and hold the rest of the body – the muscles and organs – in place.

2 **Movement** – the skeleton helps the body move by providing anchor points for the muscles to pull against, so when muscles contract, we move.

3 **Protection of vital organs** – certain parts of the skeleton surround and protect the body's organs from external forces, for example the brain is protected by the cranium, and the ribs protect the heart and lungs. This function is especially important in activities that involve contact, such as rugby or boxing.

4 **Storage of minerals** – bone stores several **minerals**, including calcium and phosphorus.

5 **Blood cell production** – the inner marrow of bones such as the sternum and ribs produce red and white blood cells. Red blood cells are important in activities because they carry oxygen to the working muscles. White blood cells are important to fight off infections in order to keep healthy.

6 **Shape** – the skeleton gives us our general shape, such as height and build. Tall people have longer leg bones and larger vertebrae. People with a heavy build have larger clavicles and bigger pelvises.

Key word

Minerals: substances that cannot be made by living things. Some minerals are essential for the human body.

Activity

Use the internet (www.tinyurl.com/y9j9wey3) to find and print an image of the skeleton. Label the diagram to identify the six different functions of bones.

Activity

Copy and complete the table.

Function	How it does this	Example
Support		
	Muscles are attached to the skeleton and can pull bones	
		The cranium protects the brain
	Some long bones contain bone marrow	
Shape		

Activity

Use the first letter of the six functions of the skeleton and create an acronym (saying or abbreviation) that uses those six letters.

Test yourself

1 Name the six functions of the skeleton.
2 Name the type of blood cells produced by the ribs.
3 Name two bones that protect vital organs.
4 Name the minerals stored in bones.

1.1.3 Types of bones

There are five types of bones in the human body. These are long bones, short bones, flat bones, sesamoid bones and the irregular bones.

Long bones

Long bones are some of the longest bones in the body, such as the **femur** and **humerus**.

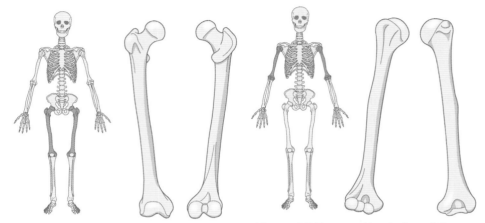

Figure 1.4 Front and back view of the femur

Figure 1.5 Front and back view of the humerus

Long bones are mainly used for movement, and the ends of long bone are covered in cartilage to absorb shock and help protect the bone. Several long bones contain bone marrow, which produces red and white blood cells.

Flat bones

Flat bones are strong, flat plates of bone. Their main function is to protect the body's vital organs and to be anchor points for muscle attachment. Examples of flat bones include the **scapula**, **sternum** and the **ribs**. In adults, most red blood cells are formed in flat bones.

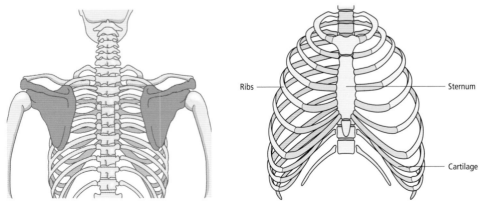

Figure 1.6 The scapula

Figure 1.7 The ribs and sternum

Short bones

Short bones are roughly as wide as they are long. Their main function is to provide support and stability with little movement. Examples of short bones are the **carpals** in the wrist and the **tarsals** in the foot.

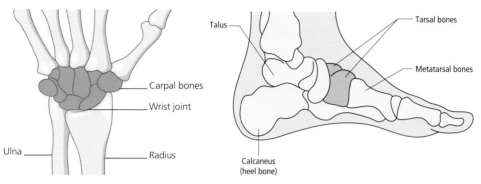

Figure 1.8 Carpals

Figure 1.9 Tarsals

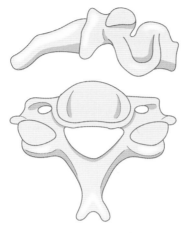

Figure 1.10 Vertebrae (seen form the side and from above)

Sesamoid bones

A sesamoid bone is found within a tendon. It protects the joint and gives a smooth surface for the tendon to move over. For example, the patella protects the knee joint.

Irregular bones

These are bones in the body which do not fall into any other category, due to their non-uniform shape. The **vertebrae**, which come in several different shapes, are examples of these. The vertebrae protect the spinal cord.

Activity

Copy and complete the table.

Types of bone	Function	Examples
		Femur, tibia, humerus
Short bones		
	Provide large area for muscles to attach to and protect organs	
Irregular bones		

Test yourself

1 Name the five types of bone.
2 Name two examples of long bones.
3 Name the main functions of short bones.
4 Name three flat bones.

Activity

Use the internet (www.tinyurl.com/y9j9wey3) to find and print an image of the skeleton. Label the diagram to identify the location of the four types of bone.

1.1.4 Types of joints

A **joint** is where two or more bones meet. There are three main types of joints: **fixed joints**, **slightly moveable joints** and **synovial joints**.

Fixed joints

Some of your joints, like those in your **skull** and in your **pelvis**, are fixed and do not allow any movement. The bones that form the joint are held together with fibrous connective tissue.

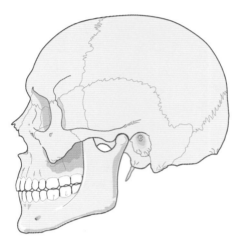

Figure 1.11 Skull

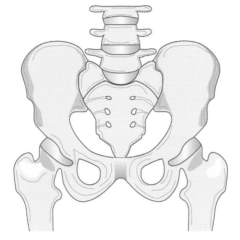

Figure 1.12 Pelvis

Slightly moveable joints

Bones that form slightly movable joints are separated by a layer of fibrous connective tissue called **cartilage**. For example, the joints formed between the **vertebrae** in your backbone contain discs of cartilage. This arrangement between the vertebrae allows for limited movement.

Synovial joints

In a **synovial joint** the bones are joined together with a fibrous joint capsule that surrounds the ends of the bones forming the joint. The fibrous capsule forms a synovial cavity that encloses the ends of the bones and this cavity is filled with **synovial fluid** that is produced by a synovial membrane. This fluid allows synovial joints to move freely.

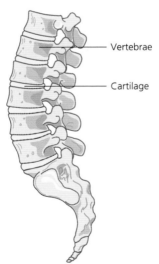

— Vertebrae

— Cartilage

Figure 1.13 Slightly moveable joints between vertebrae

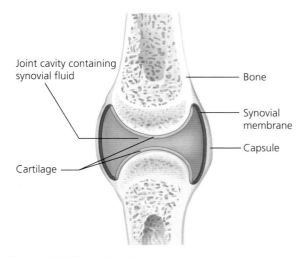

Figure 1.14 Synovial joint

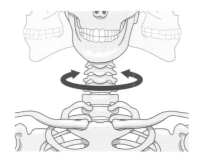

Figure 1.15 Pivot joint

There are six types of synovial joint in our skeletons.

A **pivot joint**, for example the joint between the first and second **vertebrae** of the neck, is where the rounded end of one bone fits into a ring formed by the other bone. This allows rotational or turning movements. This allows the head to rotate.

The **wrist** is a **condyloid joint** where the curved surface of the **carpal** bones join with the **radius** of the forearm. The joint allows the wrist to move from side to side as well as forwards and back.

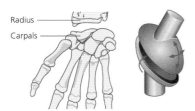

Figure 1.16 Condyloid joint

The **thumb** forms a **saddle joint**, where one of the bones forming the joint is shaped like a saddle with the other bone resting on it like a rider on a horse. This type of joint allows your thumb to move towards your fingers.

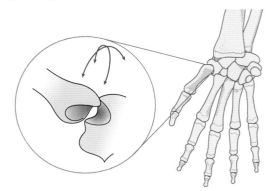

Figure 1.17 Saddle joint

Gliding joints allow some limited side to side and back and forth movements between the almost flat surfaces of the bones in the joint. The joint between the **clavicle** and the **scapula** is a gliding joint.

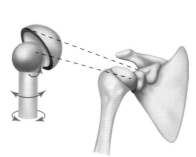

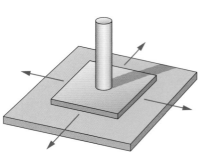

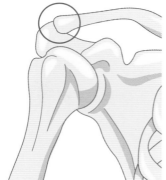

Figure 1.19 Ball and socket joint at the shoulder

Figure 1.18 Gliding joint between scapula and clavicle

Ball and socket joints have a rounded surface of one bone moving within a depression on another bone. This allows the joint to move in three different directions, forward and back, side to side and rotation. The **shoulder** and **hip** are both examples of a ball and socket joint.

A **hinge joint** is where the bones in the joint are shaped so that movement is only possible in one direction, forwards and back. The **elbow** and **knee** are both examples of hinge joints.

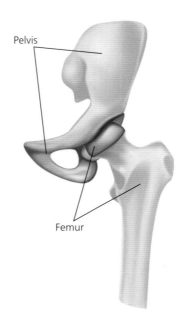

Figure 1.20 Ball and socket joint at the hip

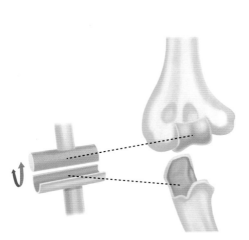

Figure 1.21 Hinge joint at the elbow

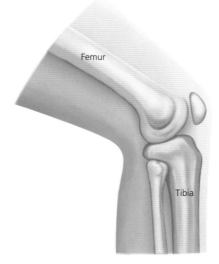

Figure 1.22 Hinge joint at the knee

Activity

Use the internet (www. tinyurl.com/y9j9wey3) to find and print an image of the skeleton. Label the diagram to identify the location of examples of the six types of synovial joint.

Activity

Work with a partner. One of you writes the name of a type of synovial joint on a sticky label; the other then adds the names of the bones forming the joint before placing the sticky label on their body to show the location of the joint.

Activity

Copy and complete the table.

Type of synovial joint	Description	Example
Pivot		
		Wrist
Gliding		Thumb
	Allows movement in three different directions	
		Elbow

Activity

Use the first letter of the six types of synovial joint and create an acronym (saying or abbreviation) that uses those six letters.

Test yourself

1 Name the six types of synovial joint.
2 Name the type of joint found at the wrist, and at the clavicle.
3 Name an example of a pivot joint and a saddle joint.
4 Name two examples of ball and socket joints.
5 Name two examples of hinge joints.

1.1.5 Joint actions

Scientists use technical terms for the movements, more properly known as **joint actions**, that have already been described in the previous pages.

Flexion: this refers to movement where the angle between two bones decreases. Flexion is commonly known as bending. When you bend your arm at the elbow, the movement is flexion.

Extension: this refers to movement where the angle between two bones increases. Extension is otherwise known as straightening. When you straighten your leg at the knee, the movement is extension.

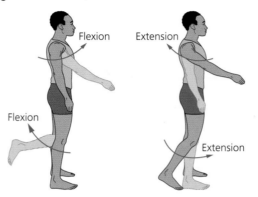

Figure 1.23 Flexion and extension

Rotation: this refers to a pivoting or twisting movement. When you turn your head to the side, this is rotation.

Adduction: this is the movement of part of the body towards the midline of the body. When you bring your legs together from an astride position, this is adduction.

Abduction: this is movement of part of the body away from the midline of the body. When you raise your arms to the side, this is abduction.

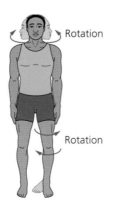

Figure 1.24 Rotation

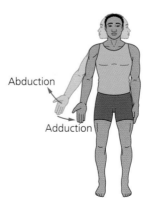

Figure 1.25 Abduction and adduction

Key words

Rotation: movement where a whole limb or part of the body turns or revolves around its length.

Adduction: movement where a part of the body is brought towards the midline of the body, for example bringing the arms into the sides.

Abduction: movement where a part of the body is taken away from the midline of the body, for example moving the legs apart.

Activity

Work with a partner. One of you names a movement and a joint; the other then demonstrates that movement at that joint.

Activity

Use the first letter of the five types of movement and create an acronym (saying or abbreviation) that uses those five letters.

Activity

Copy and complete the table.

Movement type	Joint	Sporting example
Flexion		Biceps curl
Extension		
Adduction	Shoulder	
Abduction		Bowler in cricket
Rotation		Tennis serve

Test yourself

1 Name the movements possible at the elbow.
2 Describe the movements of abduction and adduction.
3 Describe rotation of the leg.

Activity 🕖

Use the internet to find and print a copy of an unlabelled synovial joint (for example www.tinyurl.com/yb5jb9q6). Label the diagram you have printed.

1.1.6 Structure of a synovial joint (the knee)

Look again at the structure of synovial joints in Figure 1.14.

Synovial joints have a fluid-filled space between smooth cartilage pads at the end of the bones that form the joint. These pads are called **articulating cartilage** (articulating means 'forming a joint').

Surrounding the joint is a tough fibrous **joint capsule** that is lined with a **synovial membrane**. The outer layer of the joint capsule often includes **ligaments** that join bones to bones and strengthen the joint to prevent unnecessary movements and possible dislocations.

The synovial membrane lining the joint capsule produces **synovial fluid** that lubricates the joint and reduces friction and wear.

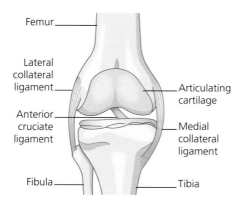

Figure 1.26 Front view of right knee showing articulating cartilage and ligaments

As well as the joint capsule and ligaments that support a synovial joint, muscles help stabilise joints because the **tendons** that attach muscles to bone are often found crossing over the joint.

For example, when the quadriceps muscle contracts, it causes extension of the knee. Although the muscle is alongside the femur, the tendon of the muscle is attached to the tibia, so when the quadriceps contract they pull on the tibia, causing extension.

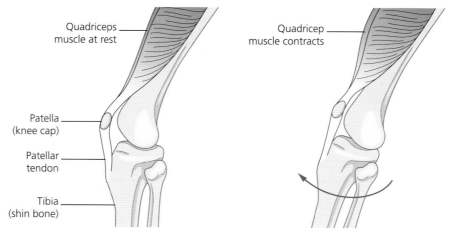

Figure 1.27 Side view of knee to show action of quadriceps muscle

When the hamstrings muscle contracts, it causes flexion at the knee. This is because the hamstring, although the hamstrings muscle is located on the back of the femur, its tendons are attached to the tibia and fibula, so when the hamstrings muscle contracts, it pulls on the tibia and fibula, causing flexion.

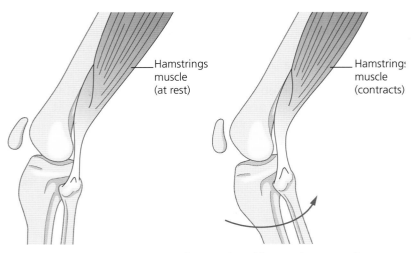

Hamstrings muscle (at rest)

Hamstrings muscle (contracts)

Figure 1.28 Side view of knee to show action of hamstrings muscle

Activity

Copy and complete the table.

Part of synovial joint	Description and role
Synovial membrane	
	Acts as a lubricant to reduce friction between the parts of the joint, preventing wear and tear
Ligament	
	Strong material that covers the ends of bones and acts as a cushion
Tendon	

Test yourself

1 Label a diagram of a synovial joint.
2 Describe the function of the joint capsule and ligaments.
3 Describe the function of the synovial membrane and synovial fluid.
4 Describe the function of the articulating cartilage.
5 Explain the action of the quadriceps and hamstrings muscles.

1.1.7 Structure of the spine and posture

The spine is made of 33 individual bones stacked one on top of the other. The spine provides the main support for your body, allowing you to stand upright, bend, and twist, while at the same time, protecting the spinal cord from injury.

Strong muscles and bones, flexible tendons and ligaments contribute to a healthy spine. However, if any of these structures is affected by strain, injury, or disease, it can cause pain.

There are the 33 individual vertebrae that interlock with each other to form the spine. The vertebrae are divided into regions: **cervical**, **thoracic**, **lumbar**, **sacrum**, and **coccyx**.

Key words

Cervical: neck vertebrae.
Thoracic: chest vertebrae; attached to ribs.
Lumbar: lower back vertebrae; weight-bearing.
Sacrum: attached to pelvis.
Coccyx: lowest part of spine; allows attachment of ligaments and muscles.

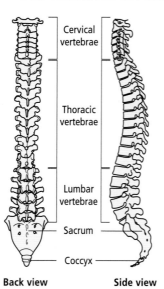

Cervical vertebrae
Thoracic vertebrae
Lumbar vertebrae
Sacrum
Coccyx

Back view   **Side view**

Figure 1.29 The regions of the spine

The main function of the **cervical** vertebrae is to support the weight of the head. The neck has two specialised vertebrae that connect to the skull and provide a large range of movement. The top cervical vertebra is ring-shaped and connects directly to the skull. This joint allows for the nodding or 'yes' motion of the head. The next vertebra down is peg-shaped and that allows the top vertebrae to pivot for the side-to-side or 'no' motion of the head.

The main function of the **thoracic** vertebrae is to hold the rib cage and protect the heart and lungs. The thoracic vertebrae have a limited range of movement.

The main function of the **lumbar** vertebrae is to bear the weight of the body. These vertebrae are much larger than other vertebrae to absorb the stress of lifting and carrying heavy objects.

The **sacrum** consists of several fused vertebrae. The main function of the sacrum is to connect the spine to the pelvis.

The **coccyx** contains several fused bones that provide attachment for ligaments and muscles of the pelvis.

Posture

The term **posture** is used to describe how your body is positioned when you are sitting, standing and lying down.

Good posture is important because it places your body in a position where the stress on supporting ligaments, tendons and muscles is limited. Good posture allows your muscles to work efficiently, which decreases wear and tear on your joints, and this decreases the risk of joint discomfort and injuries.

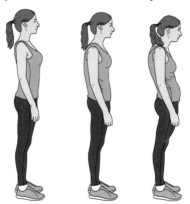

Figure 1.30 Different postures

Poor posture means your muscles and ligaments are unable to work properly and too much stress is placed on certain muscles. Poor posture can be caused by weak or tight muscles, which may prevent you from holding your body and hips in proper alignment.

Common causes of poor posture include sitting for too long, obesity, pregnancy and wearing high-heeled shoes. Long-term poor posture effects include problems with bodily systems such as digestion and breathing.

Everyone has some degree of bend in their spine. Our spines curve in in the lumbar region and out in the thoracic region.

However, an excessive thoracic bend is considered **kyphosis**, where the top of the back appears more rounded than normal. **Lordosis** is defined as an excessive inward curve of the lumbar region of the spine. **Scoliosis** is a sideways curve of the spine.

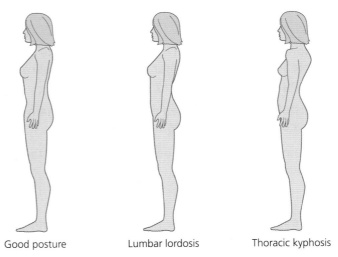

Good posture   Lumbar lordosis   Thoracic kyphosis

Figure 1.31 Lordosis and kyphosis

Activity

Copy and complete the table.

Part of spine	Function
	Has two specialised vertebrae that connect to the skull and provide a large range of movement
Thoracic	
	These vertebrae are much larger than other vertebrae to absorb the stress of lifting and carrying heavy objects
Sacrum	
	Contains several fused bones that provide attachment for ligaments and muscles of the pelvis

Test yourself

1 Label a diagram to show the different parts of the spine.
2 Describe the function of the different vertebrae found in the spine.
3 Describe the main benefits of good posture.
4 Describe the main problems associated with poor posture.
5 Explain the difference between lordosis and kyphosis.

Remember

- There are two parts to the skeleton; the axial skeleton and the appendicular skeleton.
- The axial skeleton contains the cranium, the sternum, the ribs and the vertebrae.
- The appendicular skeleton contains the bones of the arms, including the clavicle, the scapula, the humerus, the radius, the ulna, the carpals and the phalanges; and the legs, including the pelvis, the femur, the tibia, the fibula, the tarsals and the phalanges.
- There are six functions of the skeleton, including support, movement, protection, storage, production and shape.
- There are four types of bone in the skeleton, including long, flat, short and irregular bones.
- There are six types of synovial joint in the skeleton, including pivot, gliding, saddle, condyloid, hinge, and ball and socket joints.
- There are five types of movement at joints, including flexion, extension, adduction, abduction and rotation.
- Synovial joints contain an articulating capsule, synovial membrane and fluid, a joint capsule and ligaments.
- Contraction of muscles allows tendons to pull on bones; the quadriceps muscle causes knee extension, and the hamstrings cause knee flexion.
- The spine consists of five different types of vertebrae/regions: cervical, thoracic, lumbar, sacrum, coccyx.
- Good posture is important for good health as it avoids placing too much strain on ligaments, tendons and muscles.
- Poor posture can lead to lordosis or kyphosis.

Review questions

1. List the correct name for the thigh bone, the shin bone and the wrist bones.
2. List the correct name for the collar bone, the shoulder blade and the finger bones.
3. List the bones found in the forearm and the lower leg.
4. Name the minerals stored in the skeleton.
5. List the types of blood produced by the skeleton.
6. Name three sports where the skeleton's function of protection is important.
7. Name three bones that help determine our shape.
8. State the type of bone of the following: femur, vertebrae, tarsals.
9. List the two functions of long bone.
10. Identify the two functions for short bones.
11. List two types of bone that provide protection.
12. State the type of synovial joint found at the elbow and the wrist.
13. List the bones that form the hip and shoulder joints.
14. Identify the two movements possible at condyloid joints.
15. List the different types of joint that can be found in the appendicular skeleton.
16. Name the action that occurs at the knee during a sprint start.
17. Name the action that occurs at the elbow in the upward phase of a biceps curl.
18. State the types of movement that occur in the legs during jumping jacks/astride jumps.
19. Identify the movements occurring at the shoulder during breaststroke swimming.
20. List the different types of movement possible at the shoulder joint.
21. State the function of ligaments and tendons.
22. State the function of synovial fluid. How is it produced?
23. Describe the components of a synovial joint that help to keep the joint stable.
24. Name the muscle that causes knee flexion.
25. State the main functions of the different types of vertebrae.
26. Identify the parts of the spine that are attached to the pelvis.
27. Describe why good posture is important
28. Distinguish between lordosis and kyphosis.

1.2 Muscular system

1.2.1 Types of muscle

There are three types of muscle found in the human body: **Cardiac** (heart) muscle, **smooth muscle**, and **skeletal muscle**.

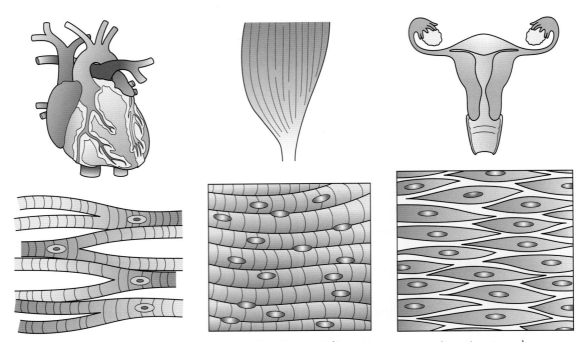

Figure 1.32 Types of muscle: cardiac, skeletal and smooth (found in organs such as the uterus)

Key words

Involuntary muscle: muscle that we have no control over.

Striated: striped muscle.

Unstriated: unstriped muscle.

Cardiac muscle

This type of muscle is only found in the walls of the heart; it is highly specialised. It is not under conscious control; it is **involuntary**. It is similar to skeletal muscle in that it is **striated** (striped).

Cardiac muscle is very resistant to fatigue, but it is dependent on a good supply of oxygen and therefore needs a good blood supply.

It is the cardiac muscle that contracts when our heart beats. The beating of the heart aids blood flow through the heart and forces blood around the body.

Smooth muscle

This type of muscle is also an involuntary muscle, but it is **unstriated**, as it does not have the stripy appearance of cardiac or skeletal muscle. Smooth muscle is found in the walls of many organs in the body, such as the digestive tract, lungs and in the walls of blood vessels.

Smooth muscle is able to contract without oxygen.

When stimulated, smooth muscle has slow, rhythmical contractions in all directions, and is used in controlling internal organs (for example, moving food along during digestion or helping with the distribution of blood).

Skeletal muscle

Skeletal muscles are those which attach to bones, and have the main function of contracting to assist movement of the bones in our skeleton. They are sometimes known as striated muscles due to their appearance.

Skeletal muscles are also sometimes called **voluntary** muscles, because we can control their contractions through nervous impulses being sent from the brain to the muscle.

Skeletal muscles can work with or without oxygen.

The contractions they produce can vary from powerful, fast movements to small precision actions. Skeletal muscles also have the ability to stretch or contract and still return to their original shape.

Key word

Voluntary muscle: muscle that we can control.

Activity

Copy and complete the table.

	Cardiac muscle	Smooth muscle	Skeletal muscle
Location			
Striated/unstriated			
Voluntary/ involuntary			
Oxygen needed/ not needed			
Functions			

Test yourself

1 Identify the three types of muscle found in the body.
2 Identify where the three types of muscle are found in the body.
3 Describe the characteristics of cardiac muscle.
4 Describe the characteristics of smooth muscle.
5 Describe the characteristics of skeletal muscle.
6 Describe the functions of cardiac muscle.
7 Describe the functions of smooth muscle.
8 Describe the functions of skeletal muscle.

1.2.2 Structure of the muscular system

Muscles move by contracting and pulling on bones. The bones then move at joints. Each of the muscles identified below cause movement when they contract.

The main skeletal muscles forming the upper body are the **deltoid, trapezius, latissimus dorsi, pectoralis major, biceps, triceps** and **rectus abdominis**.

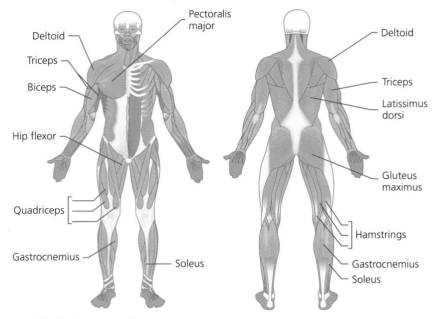

Figure 1.33 Skeletal muscles

The main **skeletal muscles** of the lower body are the **gluteus maximus, hip flexors, quadriceps, hamstrings, gastrocnemius** and **soleus**.

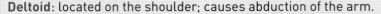

Key words

Deltoid: located on the shoulder; causes abduction of the arm.
Trapezius: located on the neck; causes extension of the head.
Latissimus dorsi: located on the back; causes adduction of the arm.
Pectoralis major: located on the chest; causes adduction of the arm.
Biceps: located on the front of the upper arm; cause flexion at the elbow.
Triceps: located on the back of the upper arm; cause extension at the elbow.
Rectus abdominis: located on the stomach wall; causes flexion of the trunk and hips.
Gluteus maximus: located on the buttocks; causes extension of the hips.
Hip flexors: located on the front of the upper legs; cause flexion of the legs.
Quadriceps: located on the front of the upper leg; cause extension at the knee.
Hamstrings: located on the back of the upper leg; cause flexion at the knee.
Gastrocnemius: located on the back of the lower legs; causes straightening of the ankle.
Soleus: located on the back of the lower legs; causes straightening of the ankle.

The **deltoid** muscle fits like a triangular cap on top of the shoulder joint. Contraction of this muscle causes abduction of the arms

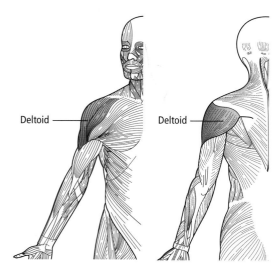

Figure 1.34 Deltoid muscle

The **trapezius** muscle is shaped like a pair of triangles, with angles on the skull, the thoracic vertebrae and the scapula. Contraction of this muscle causes extension of the skull.

The **latissimus dorsi** muscle is one of the largest muscles in the back. The muscle is divided into two halves, located in the middle of the back, and it is partially covered by the trapezius. The muscle is also attached to, and pulls against, the humerus, causing adduction.

The **pectoralis major** is a fan-shaped muscle, located on the front of the chest. It makes up the bulk of the chest muscles and is also attached to, and pulls against, the humerus, causing adduction.

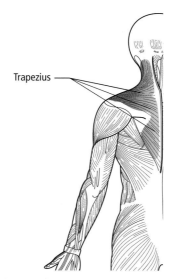

Figure 1.35 Trapezius muscle

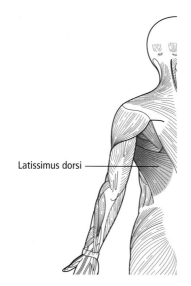

Figure 1.36 Latissimus dorsi muscle

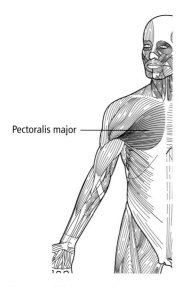

Figure 1.37 Pectoralis major muscle

The **biceps** muscle is the muscle on the front part of the upper arm. The biceps is attached to the shoulder and pulls on the radius to cause flexion at the elbow.

The **triceps** muscle is a large muscle on the back of the upper arm. It is the muscle principally responsible for extension of the elbow joint.

The **rectus abdominis** muscles, commonly called the 'abs', are a pair of long, flat muscles that extend along the entire length of the abdomen. Each muscle consists of a line of four fleshy muscular bodies connected by tendons, which give it a lumpy appearance when well defined and tensed. This lumpy appearance results in the rectus abdominis muscles being referred to as the 'six-pack' (it really should be called an eight-pack!).

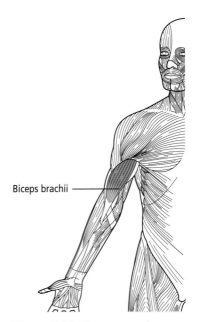

Figure 1.38 Biceps muscle

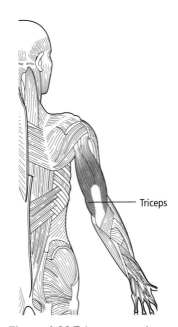

Figure 1.39 Triceps muscle

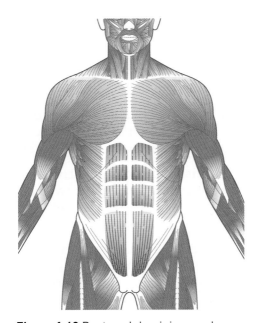

Figure 1.40 Rectus abdominis muscle

The **gluteus maximus** is the main muscle causing extension of the hip. It makes up a large portion of the shape and appearance of each side of the hips, forming the buttocks.

The **hip flexor** muscles are attached to the pelvis to allow flexion of the femur.

The **quadriceps** are a large group of muscles in front of the thigh, the action of which causes extension of the leg.

The **hamstrings** are the large set of powerful muscles that span the back of the thigh from the buttocks to the calves and cause flexion at the knee.

The **gastrocnemius muscle** is located on the back of the lower leg, being one of the two major muscles that make up the calf. The other major calf muscle is the **soleus**. This is a flat muscle that lies underneath the gastrocnemius. Both the gastrocnemius and the soleus run the entire length of the lower leg, connecting behind the knee and at the heel. When contracting, the gastrocnemius and soleus cause the ankle to straighten and the toes to point.

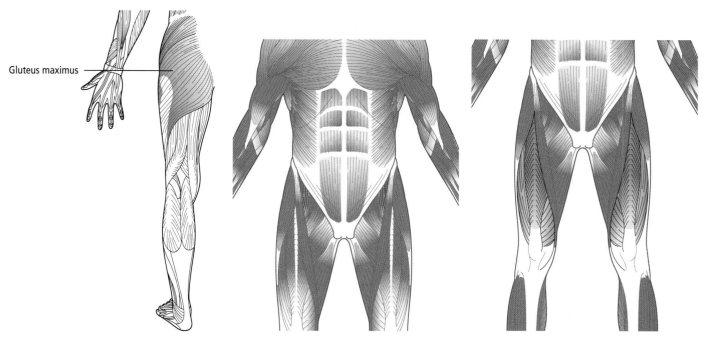

Figure 1.41 Gluteus maximus muscle **Figure 1.42** Hip flexor muscle **Figure 1.43** Quadriceps muscle

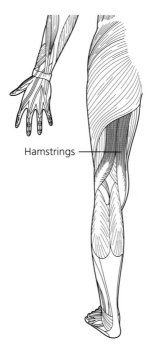

Figure 1.44 Hamstrings muscle

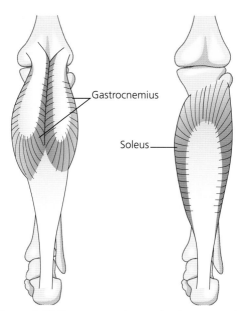

Figure 1.45 Gastrocnemius and soleus muscles

We can look at how muscles, bones and joints work together by considering movements that occur at the elbow.

To bend our arm at the elbow, the biceps contract. The biceps muscle is attached to the radius bone in the lower arm, and as it contracts, it pulls on the radius and causes flexion at the elbow.

To straighten our arm at the elbow, the triceps contract. The triceps muscle is attached to the ulna bone in the lower arm, and as it contracts it pulls on the ulna and causes extension at the elbow.

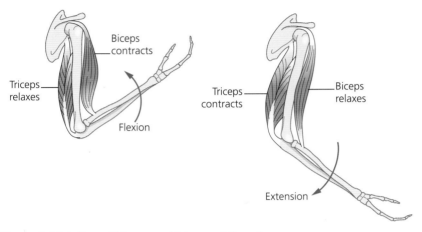

Figure 1.46 Action of biceps and triceps at the elbow

Activity

Print a copy of Figure 1.33. Alongside the names of the muscles labelled on the figure, write the main action that contraction of that muscle causes.

A similar mechanism operates at the knee. To straighten our leg at the knee, the quadriceps muscle contracts. The muscle is attached to the front of the tibia of the lower leg and as it contracts it pulls on the front of the tibia and causes extension at the knee.

To bend our leg at the knee, the hamstrings contract. The hamstrings are attached to the back of the tibia, and as the hamstrings muscle contracts it pulls on the back of the tibia and causes flexion at the knee.

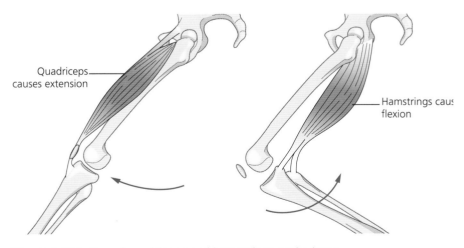

Figure 1.47 Action of quadriceps and hamstrings at the knee

Activity

Copy and complete the table.

Name of muscle	Main action	Sporting action
Deltoid	Abduction of the shoulder	
	Rotates shoulders; extension of head	Swimmer turning head to breathe
Latissimus dorsi		Swimming strokes
Pectoralis major	Adduction of shoulder	
Biceps		Drawing a bow in archery
	Extension at the elbow	
Rectus abdominis		Performing sit-ups
	Extension of hip	Moving lead and trail leg in hurdling
Hip flexors		Lifting knees during sprint
	Extension at the knee	
Hamstrings		Pulling back of the knee prior to kicking a ball
Gastrocnemius	Straightens ankle; points toes	Take-off for basketball layup
Soleus		Jumping to block at volleyball

Test yourself

1 Name the muscles that cause flexion and extension at the knee and elbow.
2 Identify the actions of the deltoid, latissimus dorsi, pectoralis major and trapezius muscles.
3 Describe the actions of the rectus abdominis, gluteus maximus and hip flexor muscles.
4 Describe the actions of the gastrocnemius and soleus muscles.

Activity

Create a video of the following physical activities, identifying the main muscles, joints and bones that are involved in the movements.
- bending and straightening your arm at the elbow
- bending and straightening your leg at the knee
- performing 'jumping jacks'/'astride jumps'
- completing a 'squat'.

1.2.3 Muscle movement and contraction

Muscle action

Muscles can only contract and pull bones. Therefore, joints need to have two muscles working opposite each other – one to pull the bones in one direction and another to pull the bones in the opposite direction.

As one muscle contracts, the second muscle relaxes. As the second muscle contracts, so the first muscle relaxes. This is known as antagonistic muscle action.

An example of this is found in the upper arm. The triceps and biceps are on opposite sides of the humerus. When the biceps contract, the lower arm (radius and ulna) moves up towards the shoulder. The triceps relax to allow this movement to happen. In this action, the biceps muscle is the contracting muscle or **agonist**, while the triceps muscle is the relaxing muscle or **antagonist**.

There are two types of muscle contraction: isotonic and isometric.

Isotonic

Isotonic contractions occur when the muscle changes length as it contracts and causes movement of a body part.

There are two types of isotonic contraction. **Concentric** contractions are those where the muscle shortens as it contracts. An example is bending the elbow from straight to fully flexed, caused by a concentric contraction of the biceps muscle. Concentric contractions are the most common type of muscle contraction and occur frequently in sporting activities.

Eccentric contractions occur when the muscle lengthens as it contracts. This is less common than a concentric contraction and usually involves the control or slowing down of a movement.

In the downward phase of a press-up, the triceps contract eccentrically to slow the movement down.

Similarly, in a squat, the quadriceps contract eccentrically to lower the body slowly towards the ground.

> **Key words**
>
> **Agonist**: the contracting muscle; the muscle that causes movement.
> **Antagonist**: muscle that relaxes to allow the agonist to contract.
> **Isotonic**: muscle action where the muscle changes length – causes movement.
> **Concentric**: isotonic contraction where the muscle shortens.
> **Eccentric**: isotonic contraction where the muscle lengthens – used to control downward movements.

Isometric

During **isometric** contractions, the muscle remains the same length. For example, while performing a headstand, many of the body's muscles are contracting, but there is no movement as the balance is being held.

If we consider again the movements of flexion and extension at the elbow. During elbow flexion, the biceps act as the agonist and the triceps as the antagonist. During elbow extension, the triceps become the working muscle (the agonist) and the biceps relax and act as the antagonist.

If you perform the weight training exercise known as the biceps curl, the biceps contract in three different ways.

- During the elbow flexion stage of the movement, the biceps are contracting concentrically. The biceps are shortening as they contract.

- During extension of the elbow, the biceps are contracting to slow the movement down and are lengthening. This is an eccentric contraction of the biceps.

- In-between these two actions there is a short rest period, where the elbows are fully flexed and no movement is taking place. At this time the biceps are contracting, without movement: an isometric contraction.

> **Key word** 🔑
>
> **Isometric**: muscle action where the muscle stays the same length – used in balances.

Figure 1.48 Downward phase of a press-up; the triceps contracts eccentrically

Figure 1.49 Downward phase of a squat; the quadriceps contracts eccentrically

Figure 1.50 Biceps curl; the biceps contract in three different ways

Activity

Work with a partner. You need a barbell or a pair of dumbbells of sufficient weight to enable you to perform a biceps curl without difficulty. The biceps curl involves two movements; flexion/an upward movement and extension/a downward movement. One of the pair (the tester) places their hands on their partner's upper arm, one hand feeling the biceps, the other feeling the triceps. Their partner (the subject) performs flexion while holding the barbell/dumbbells, while the tester decides through touch/pressure which muscle is working. The working muscle (agonist) will change shape during contraction and become firmer to touch. The subject should repeat the flexion movement of the biceps curl if necessary.

Having decided which muscle is the agonist during flexion, the subject begins performing extension at the elbow, and again the tester must decide, through feeling for increased firmness/tension in the muscles, which muscle is the agonist during elbow extension.

Copy and complete the table.

Action	Agonist	Movement
Biceps curl – flexion		
Biceps curl – extension		

Activity

Print a copy of Figure 1.49. Label the main muscles involved in the movement. Identify the main agonist contracting, and the type of contraction occurring at the knee and the hip during the upward phase of the movement. Then repeat for the downward phase of the movement.

Copy and complete the table.

	Joint	Action	Agonist	Movement
Upward phase	Knee			
Upward phase	Hip			

	Joint	Action	Agonist	Movement
Downward phase	Knee			
Downward phase	Hip			

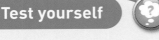

Test yourself

1 Name the agonist and antagonist muscles that cause flexion at the knee and elbow.

2 Distinguish between isotonic and isometric muscle contractions.

3 Distinguish between concentric and eccentric muscle contractions.

1.2.4 Muscle fibre types

Muscles are made up of thread-like muscle fibres. Individual muscles contain different muscle fibre types – **type 1 slow-twitch fibres** and **type 2 fast-twitch fibres**. Each fibre type has different qualities in the way they work and how quickly they fatigue.

Type 1 slow-twitch fibres are red in colour because of their rich supply of oxygen. Type 1 muscle fibres are very resistant to fatigue and are capable of producing repeated slow contractions.

For this reason, the muscles containing mainly type 1 fibres are often muscles involved in maintaining posture, such as those in the neck and back, due to their endurance capabilities. Also, athletes such as marathon runners tend to have a high number of this type of muscle fibre (as explained below), because that event requires repeated slow contractions of muscles that are resistant to fatigue.

Type 2 fast-twitch fibres are white in colour, due to having a low level of oxygen. They are capable of producing fast contractions and bursts of power, but this results in rapid fatigue.

This type of fibre is found mainly in the muscles of the arms and legs, where they can be used for fast, powerful contractions. Different people are born with different proportions of type 1 and type 2 muscle fibres, and these proportions cannot be changed. However, training will affect the different muscle fibre types. For example, marathon runners train by running many miles at a slow pace. This benefits their type 1 slow-twitch fibres and makes these muscle fibres even more resistant to fatigue. Similarly, sprinters train by running very fast, and this benefits the type 2 fast-twitch fibres, enabling these muscle fibres to produce even more rapid and powerful contractions.

Key words

Type 1 slow-twitch fibres: muscle fibre that is red, contracts slowly and is resistant to fatigue.

Type 2 fast-twitch fibres: muscle fibre that is white, contracts rapidly and fatigues easily.

Test yourself

1. Name the two types of muscle fibre.
2. Distinguish between type 1 slow-twitch fibres and type 2 fast-twitch muscle fibres.
3. What type of activities are best suited to using type 1 slow-twitch fibres?
4. What type of activities do you think are best suited to using type 2 fast-twitch fibres?

Activity

Copy and complete the table.

Characteristic	Type 1 slow-twitch fibres	Type 2 fast-twitch fibres
Speed of contraction		
Colour		
Resistance to fatigue		
Activity suited to		

Remember

- There are three types of muscle – cardiac, smooth and skeletal.
- Cardiac muscle is striated, involuntary, needs oxygen and is found in the heart.
- Smooth muscle is unstriated, involuntary, does not need oxygen and is found in organs and blood vessels.
- Skeletal muscle is striated, voluntary, can work with or without oxygen, and causes movement of the skeleton.
- Muscles pull on the skeleton to cause movement.
- Flexion at the elbow is due to action of the biceps; extension is caused by the triceps.
- Flexion at the knee is due to action of the hamstrings; extension is caused by the quadriceps.
- Abduction at the shoulder is due to action of the deltoids; adduction is caused by the latissimus dorsi and the pectoralis major.
- Flexion at the hip is due to action of the hip flexors; extension is caused by the gluteus maximus.
- The gastrocnemius and soleus both cause the ankle to straighten.
- The rectus abdominis causes trunk and hip flexion.
- The trapezius causes head extension.
- Muscles work in pairs to pull on the skeleton to cause movement.
- The working muscle is called the agonist, the relaxing muscle is the antagonist.
- Muscles can contract and cause movement; this is an isotonic contraction.
- Muscles can contract, but no movement occurs; this is an isometric contraction.
- During isotonic contractions, if the agonist shortens, this is called a concentric contraction; if the muscle lengthens, it is an eccentric contraction.
- Type 1 slow-twitch fibres muscle fibres are red, contract slowly and are resistant to fatigue.
- Type 2 fast-twitch fibres muscle fibres are white, contract rapidly and fatigue easily.
- Type 1 slow-twitch fibres muscle fibres are suited to activities such as long-distance running, cycling and swimming.
- Type 2 fast-twitch fibres muscle fibres are suited to sprinting, tackling and jumping.

Review questions

1 State the main characteristics of skeletal muscle.
2 Identify the parts of the body that contain smooth muscle.
3 Describe the functions of cardiac muscle.
4 Identify the type(s) of muscle that is involuntary.
5 Identify the type(s) of muscle that is striated.
6 Identify the main muscles causing the movements at the hip, knee and ankle when standing up out of a chair.
7 Identify the names of the muscles that cause adduction at the shoulder.
8 Describe the actions of the trapezius muscle.
9 State the main action caused by the hip flexors and the rectus abdominis.
10 Identify the main muscles causing the movements and the type of contraction occurring at the hip and knee when sitting down into a chair.
11 Identify the names of the agonist muscles and the type of contraction occurring during abduction and adduction at the shoulder.
12 Explain how concentric, isometric and eccentric contractions of the triceps are possible during a single press-up exercise.
13 Suggest why marathon runners tend to have a high proportion of type 1 slow-twitch muscle fibres.
14 Explain which type of muscle fibre tends to predominate in elite sprinters.
15 Explain why games players tend to need a mixture of muscle fibre types.

1.3 Respiratory system

1.3.1 Structure of the respiratory system

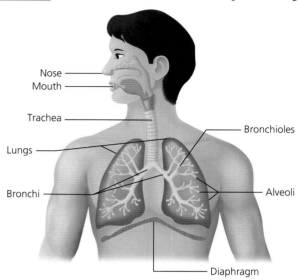

Nose
Mouth
Trachea
Bronchioles
Lungs
Bronchi
Alveoli
Diaphragm

Figure 1.51 The respiratory system

The respiratory system involves those parts of the body that are concerned with breathing.

When we breathe in, air moves through the **mouth** and **nose** and then travels through the **pharynx** and **larynx** into the **trachea** (windpipe). The trachea carries air, which contains oxygen, from the pharynx to the **lungs**.

The pharynx and larynx are the names given to the chambers at the back of the throat (pharynx) and the voice box (larynx).

The inner surface of the trachea is covered in tiny hairs called cilia, which catch particles of dust, which are then removed when coughing. The trachea is kept open by rings of cartilage.

Near the lungs, the trachea divides into two tubes called **bronchi**, one to each lung. Once inside the lung the bronchi split several ways, forming smaller and smaller bronchi.

The small bronchi further divide into **bronchioles**, which are very narrow tubes, less than 1 millimetre in diameter. There is no cartilage within the bronchioles.

At the end of each bronchiole are openings to the **alveoli**. There are usually several alveoli coming from one bronchiole, forming a little clump that resembles a cluster of grapes.

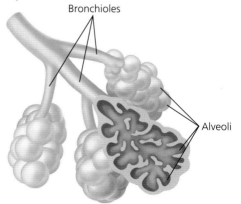

Bronchioles
Alveoli

Figure 1.52 Alveoli

Key words

Mouth and nose: air enters the body through these.

Pharynx: chamber at the back of the throat.

Larynx: voice box.

Trachea: often called the windpipe, lined with rings of cartilage and carries air from the pharynx to the bronchi.

Bronchi: two tubes that carry air from the trachea into each lung.

Bronchioles: tiny tubes that carry air to the alveoli.

Alveoli: minute air sacs in the lungs.

Activity

Rearrange the following terms into the correct order that air passes through before reaching the lungs:

bronchi, mouth, alveoli, larynx, nose, pharynx, trachea, bronchioles

Activity

Print a copy of the diagram of the respiratory system from the following link and label the parts shown: www.tinyurl.com/yczk25o6

Activity

Copy the table, but rearrange the characteristics in the correct order to match the structures.

Structure	Characteristic
Mouth and nose	Take air into each lung
Pharynx	Windpipe carrying air towards lungs
Larynx	Two large bags containing air
Trachea	Chamber at back of throat
Bronchi	Voice box
Bronchioles	Air sacs
Alveoli	Air enters the body through these
Lungs	Tiny tubes

Test yourself

1   Name the structures through which air passes on its way from the mouth to the lungs.
2   Describe the relationship between alveoli and bronchioles.

1.3.2 Functions of the respiratory system

Breathing is a two-stage process. **Inspiration** is the intake of air into the lungs, which is brought about by increasing the volume of the chest cavity. **Exhalation** is the expulsion of air from the lungs through reducing the volume of the chest cavity.

Both inspiration and exhalation involve the use of muscles. The **diaphragm** is a sheet of muscle that separates the chest from the abdomen. The **intercostal** muscles are found between the ribs. When these muscles contract they cause the chest cavity to increase in size and therefore increase its volume.

Contraction of the dome-shaped diaphragm causes it to flatten, thus enlarging the chest cavity. At the same time, contraction of the intercostal muscles causes the ribs to rise, also increasing the size of the chest cavity.

When the chest cavity expands, its volume increases. This reduces the pressure in the chest cavity and air is passively drawn into the lungs. Air passes from the higher pressure outside the lungs to the lower pressure inside the lungs.

> ### Key words
>
> **Inspiration**: breathing air in.
> **Exhalation**: breathing air out.

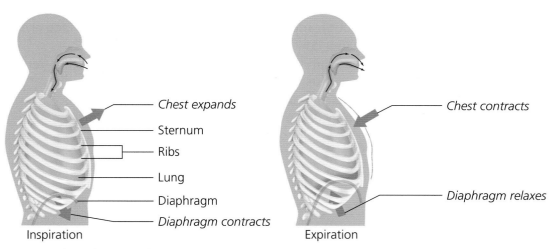

Inspiration | Expiration

- Chest expands
- Sternum
- Ribs
- Lung
- Diaphragm
- *Diaphragm contracts*
- *Chest contracts*
- *Diaphragm relaxes*

Figure 1.53 Inspiration and exhalation

During exhalation the breathing muscles relax. The diaphragm curves and returns to its dome shape; the weight of the ribs causes them to descend and the chest volume decreases.

The reduction in the size of the chest cavity increases the pressure of the air in the lungs and causes it to be expelled. Exhalation is passive; the breathing muscles simply relax. Air passes from the higher pressure in the lungs to the lower pressure in the bronchi and trachea.

Gaseous exchange

The basic function of alveoli is the exchange of gases. Capillaries carrying blood surround the alveoli. The exchange of oxygen from the lungs into the blood, and the exchange of carbon dioxide in the blood from these capillaries and into the lungs, occur through the walls of the alveoli.

Gaseous exchange at the lungs takes place by **diffusion**. The gases carbon dioxide and oxygen move down a concentration gradient from a high concentration to low concentration. This means that the oxygen in the alveoli, which is at a relatively high concentration, diffuses into the blood capillaries where the oxygen concentration is lower. The oxygen that diffuses out of the alveoli is replaced from the air that we continue to breathe in.

The same thing happens in the case of carbon dioxide. Blood in the capillaries surrounding the alveoli contains a relatively high concentration of carbon dioxide and the alveoli contain a lower concentration. Thus, carbon dioxide diffuses into the alveoli from the blood and is eventually breathed out.

The process of diffusion is a passive process and is helped by several factors:

- The surface of the alveoli and the walls of the blood capillaries are very thin (one cell thick) and moist, which helps the exchange of gases.
- The alveoli are very small in size and large in number (there are millions in each lung), and so the alveoli provide a large surface area for the exchange of gases.
- The alveoli and capillaries are touching each other so there is a very short distance for diffusion (short diffusion pathway).
- Each alveolus is surrounded by a network of blood capillaries, so there is a rich supply of blood for the gases to diffuse into/from.

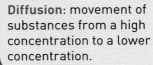

Key word

Diffusion: movement of substances from a high concentration to a lower concentration.

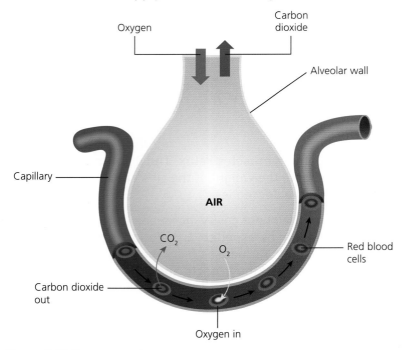

Figure 1.54 Gaseous exchange

Activity

Copy and complete the table.

	Inspiration	Exhalation
Ribcage		Moves inwards and downwards as intercostal muscles relax
Diaphragm	Contracts and becomes flatter	
Effect	Air containing oxygen is drawn into the lungs	

Activity

Copy and complete the table.

	Inspiration	Exhalation
Volume of lungs	Increases	
Pressure in lungs		Increases
Effect	Air containing oxygen is drawn into the lungs	

Test yourself

1 Name the muscles that are involved in inspiration.
2 Describe the changes in the size of the chest cavity during inspiration.
3 Describe the process of diffusion.
4 Describe the factors that assist the gaseous exchange process.

Key words

Tidal volume: amount of air that enters the lungs during normal inspiration at rest.

Residual volume: amount of air left in the lungs after a maximal exhalation.

Vital capacity: maximum amount of air you can exhale after taking the deepest possible inspiration.

1.3.3 Lung volumes

The **respiratory** or **lung volumes** are the amount of air inspired, exhaled and stored within the lungs at any given time.

These volumes include:

- The amount of air which enters the lungs during normal inspiration at rest. This is the **tidal volume**. The average tidal volume is 500 ml. The same amount leaves the lungs during exhalation.
- The amount of air left in the lungs following a maximal exhalation is called the **residual volume**. There is always some air remaining to prevent the lungs from collapsing.
- The maximum amount of air you can exhale after taking the deepest inspiration you possibly can is the **vital capacity**. It can be up to ten times more than you would normally exhale.

Table 1.1 Average lung volumes in healthy adults

	Value (litres)	
Volume	Men	Women
Tidal volume	0.5	0.5
Residual volume	1.2	1.1
Vital capacity	4.8	3.1

Lung volumes are measured using a spirometer, which is a piece of apparatus consisting of a chamber filled with oxygen that floats on a tank of water. A person breathes from a mouthpiece attached to a tube connected to the chamber.

Breathing in takes oxygen away from the chamber, which then sinks down. Breathing out then pushes air into the chamber causing it to float. During these movements, the lung volumes involved may be seen and measured.

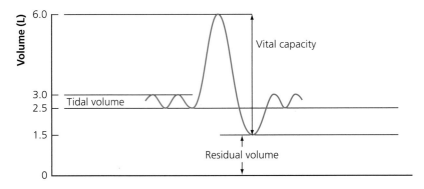

Figure 1.55 Typical spirometer trace

Activity

Copy and complete the table.

	Definition	Average value in men	Average value in women
Tidal volume			
Residual volume			
Vital capacity			

Test yourself

1 Define each of the three lung volumes.
2 Describe the differences between male and female lung volumes.

Remember

- The correct order for the passage of air into the lungs is: mouth, nose, pharynx, larynx, trachea, bronchi, bronchioles, alveoli, lungs.
- The bronchi and trachea are kept open by rings of cartilage.
- There are millions of alveoli in each lung.
- Inspiration is breathing in. Exhalation is breathing out.
- Diffusing is the process of substances moving from an area of high concentration to a lower concentration.
- Oxygen diffuses from the alveoli and into the blood. Carbon dioxide diffuses from the blood into the alveoli.

- The process of gaseous exchange is helped by the large surface area of alveoli, the thin membranes, the short distances involved and the rich blood supply.
- Tidal volume is the amount of air we breathe out at rest.
- Residual volume is the air left in our lungs after a maximum exhalation.
- Vital capacity is the maximum amount of air we can breathe out.
- Lung volumes can be recorded using a spirometer.

Review questions

1 When we breathe in, air enters our nose and mouth and passes through our pharynx and larynx. Identify the other structures that air passes through before entering our lungs.
2 Identify the muscles that cause inspiration at rest.
3 Describe the process of exhalation.
4 State three factors that assist the process of diffusion in the alveoli.

5 Explain the process of gaseous exchange.
6 Identify the lung volume that measures the amount of air left in the lungs after breathing out.
7 Which is larger: vital capacity or tidal volume?
8 Which lung volume best describes the air we normally use for breathing while at rest.

1.4 Cardiovascular system

1.4.1 Structure and function of the blood vessels

Arteries carry blood away from the heart. Most arteries carry oxygenated blood. The blood within arteries is under high pressure. Arteries are elastic; they have thick muscular walls which maintain their high blood pressure.

Small arteries have muscular walls that can adjust their diameter to increase or decrease blood flow to a particular part of the body. When the rings of muscle in the small arteries contract, it narrows those arteries and reduces the flow of blood through that artery. This is called **vasoconstriction**.

The small arteries can also widen (**vasodilation**) to allow more blood to flow through that artery to the tissues. Vasodilation occurs during exercise to allow more blood to flow to the exercising muscles. Moving blood to those parts of the body, such as the muscles, that have a greater demand for blood is called the **vascular shunt** mechanism.

The vascular shunt mechanism will direct the flow of blood to those muscles of the body involved in health and fitness activities, such as the legs during running. At the same time, less blood will be directed towards other parts of the body where demand for blood is not as great, for example, inactive muscles and organs, such as the kidneys and the stomach.

Capillaries are tiny, thin-walled blood vessels that join arteries (which carry blood away from the heart) and veins (which carry blood back to the heart). The thin walls of the capillaries allow gaseous exchange at the lungs, where oxygen passes from the alveoli into blood and carbon dioxide passes from blood into the alveoli.

Nutrients also diffuse from blood in the capillaries into the surrounding tissues, and waste products diffuse from the tissues into the blood.

Blood flows from the capillaries into very small **veins**, then into larger veins that lead back to the heart. Veins carry deoxygenated blood back to the heart. Veins have valves to ensure the blood flows in one direction.

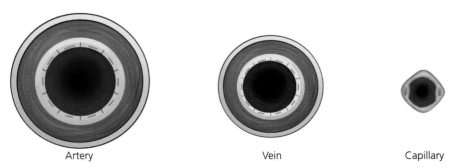

Artery   Vein   Capillary

Figure 1.56 Different types of blood vessels

Table 1.2 Differences between structure and functions of arteries, veins and capillaries

Arteries	Veins	Capillaries
Carry blood away from the heart	Carry blood towards the heart	Huge network of tiny vessels linking arteries and veins
Most (but not all) arteries carry bright red oxygenated blood	Most (but not all) veins carry dark red deoxygenated blood	Very narrow – only one red blood cell at a time
Stretch as blood surges through and then return to normal shape – they have a pulse	No stretch, no pulse	Very thin walls (one cell thick) to allow rapid diffusion of substances into and out of the blood
Thick, muscular and elastic walls to withstand pressure	Thin-walled	
Large lumen (internal diameter)	Small lumen (internal diameter)	
	Have valves to prevent backflow of blood	

Activity

Copy and complete the table.

	Arteries	Veins
Direction of travel		
Type of blood carried		
Thickness of walls		
Size of lumen		
Presence of valves		
Presence of a pulse		

Test yourself

1 List the main features of arteries, veins and capillaries.
2 Describe the different functions of arteries, veins and capillaries.
3 Describe the differences between vasoconstriction and vasodilation.
4 Suggest why we need a vascular shunt mechanism.

1.4.2 Structure of the heart

The heart is a muscular organ (about the size of a closed fist) that pumps blood around the body. It is divided into separate left and right sides, and each side has an upper and a lower chamber. The upper chambers are the **atria**, which collect blood from veins, and the lower chambers are the **ventricles**, which pump out blood through the arteries.

> ### Key words
>
> **Atria**: upper chambers of the heart that collect blood from veins.
>
> **Ventricles**: lower chambers of the heart which pump blood out of the heart to the arteries.
>
> **Vena cava**: blood vessel carrying deoxygenated blood (see below) from the body to the right atrium.
>
> **Right atrium**: heart chamber receiving deoxygenated blood from the vena cava.
>
> **Right ventricle**: heart chamber pumping deoxygenated blood into the pulmonary artery.
>
> **Pulmonary artery**: blood vessel carrying deoxygenated blood from the right ventricle to the lungs.
>
> **Pulmonary vein**: blood vessel carrying oxygenated blood from the lungs to the left atrium.
>
> **Left atrium**: heart chamber receiving oxygenated blood from the pulmonary vein.
>
> **Left ventricle**: heart chamber pumping oxygenated blood into the aorta.
>
> **Aorta**: blood vessel carrying oxygenated blood from the left ventricle to the body.
>
> **Deoxygenated blood**: blood returning to the heart/lungs lacking oxygen.

The right side of the heart takes in deoxygenated blood from the **vena cava** and passes the blood into the **right atrium**. This blood then flows into the **right ventricle** before it is pumped out of the heart, along the **pulmonary artery** to the lungs for oxygenation.

The newly oxygenated blood returns from the lungs in the **pulmonary vein** and the blood flows into the **left atrium**. The blood travels down into the **left ventricle** before it is pumped out of the heart through the **aorta** to provide oxygen and nutrients to the body tissues.

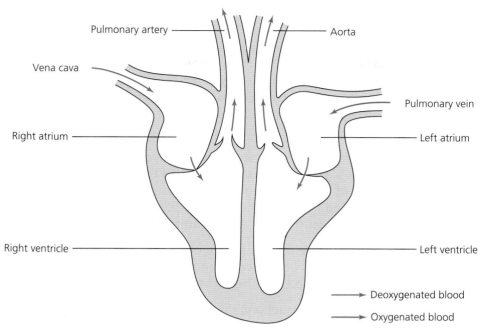

Pulmonary artery — Aorta

Vena cava —

Pulmonary vein

Right atrium — — Left atrium

Right ventricle — — Left ventricle

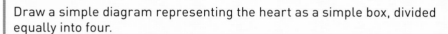 → Deoxygenated blood

→ Oxygenated blood

Figure 1.57 Structure of the heart

Activity

Draw a simple diagram representing the heart as a simple box, divided equally into four.

Colour one side red to show oxygenated blood, and the other side blue to show deoxygenated blood. Label the four small squares as the chambers of the heart and add arrows to show the flow of blood into and out of the chamber, and name each blood vessel that carries blood to and from the heart.

Test yourself

1 Name the four chambers of the heart.
2 Name the blood vessels that are attached to the four chambers of the heart.
3 Which side of the heart carries oxygenated blood?

1.4.3 The cardiac cycle

The heart beats about 70 times in a minute when we are at rest. There are two phases to a heartbeat. There is a period of relaxation when the heart fills with blood. Then the heart contracts and pumps blood to the arteries. One heartbeat is completed when the heart fills with blood and the blood is pumped out of the heart. The events that happen during a single heartbeat is called the **cardiac cycle**.

The events of a cardiac cycle described below trace the path of the blood as it enters the right side of the heart, is pumped to the lungs, travels back to the left side of the heart and is pumped out to the rest of the body. It should be noted that both the left and right sides of the heart go through relaxation and contraction at the same time.

During the relaxation phase of the cardiac cycle, the atria and ventricles are relaxed. **Deoxygenated blood** from the body flows into the **vena cava,** which carries the blood into the **right atrium**.

The heart then begins to contract and the right atrium empties its contents into the **right ventricle**. The right ventricle contracts soon after, forcing blood out of the heart along the **pulmonary artery** towards the **lungs**.

The deoxygenated blood flows through the pulmonary arteries to the lungs where gaseous exchange occurs. The blood picks up oxygen, and carbon hdioxide is removed before the blood returns to the **left atrium** of the heart through the **pulmonary vein**.

The **oxygenated blood** from the pulmonary vein fills the left atrium during the relaxation phase of the heart. The heart begins to contract again and the left atrium empties its contents into the **left ventricle**.

The left ventricle also contracts and the oxygenated blood is pumped into the **aorta** and is carried around the body, dropping off oxygen and nutrients to various tissues, while at the same time picking up waste products and becoming deoxygenated.

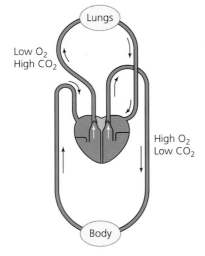

Figure 1.58 Circulation of the blood

Lungs

Low O_2
High CO_2

High O_2
Low CO_2

Body

Key word 🔑

Oxygenated blood: blood leaving the heart/lungs rich in oxygen.

Activity

Rearrange the following terms into the correct order of the cardiac cycle for the right side of the heart:

- right atrium
- pulmonary artery
- the lungs
- from the body
- deoxygenated blood
- right ventricle
- become oxygenated
- vena cava

Activity

Rearrange the following terms into the correct order of the cardiac cycle for the left side of the heart:

- become deoxygenated
- pulmonary vein
- left atrium
- aorta
- to the body
- from the lungs
- oxygenated blood
- left ventricle

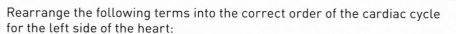

Test yourself

1 List the correct order of the cardiac cycle, starting with the vena cava and ending with the lungs.

2 List the correct order of the cardiac cycle, starting with the lungs and ending with the aorta.

1.4.4 Cardiovascular measurements

Your **heart rate** can be taken at any spot on the body where an artery is close to the surface and a pulse can be felt. The most common places to measure heart rate using this method is at the wrist (radial artery) and the neck (carotid artery).

- **Radial pulse (wrist)** – place your index and middle fingers together on the opposite wrist, about ½ inch on the inside of the joint, in line with the index finger. Once you find a pulse, count the number of beats you feel within a one-minute period.
- **Carotid pulse (neck)** – to measure your heart rate at the neck, place your first two fingers on either side of the neck until you can feel the beats. Be careful not to press too hard, then count the number of beats for a minute.

You can estimate the per minute heart rate by counting over ten seconds and multiplying this figure by six, or count over 15 seconds and multiply by four, or over 30 seconds and doubling the result.

A normal resting heart rate can range anywhere from 40 to 100 beats per minute. Your resting heart rate can vary with your fitness level and with age. The fitter you are, generally the lower your resting heart rate. This is due to the heart getting bigger and stronger with exercise, and getting more efficient at pumping blood around the body; so at rest, more blood can be pumped around with each beat, therefore fewer beats per minute are needed.

It is quite normal to use your heart rate as a guide to how hard you are exercising. The heart rate during exercise is an indicator of intensity (in other words, how hard you are working). As you get fitter, your heart rate should decrease for any given exercise workload.

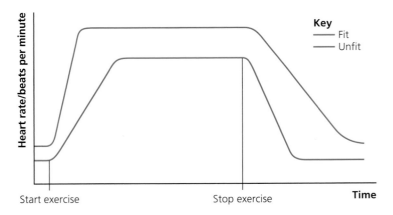

Figure 1.59 The effects of exercise on heart rate

During exercise, your heart rate will depend on the intensity of exercise, your fitness level, and your **maximum heart rate (MHR)** (which may also depend on your age). To calculate your maximum heart rate in beats per minute, use the formula:

maximum heart rate (MHR) = 220 – age

So, for example, a 16-year-old has a maximum heart rate of 220 – 16 (age) = 204.

When the heart beats, it pumps out blood into the arteries. **Cardiac output** is the volume of blood that the heart is able to pump out. It is usually measured in litres per minute. The cardiac output represents the volume of oxygenated blood that is delivered to the body.

Figure 1.60 Maximum heart rate is 220 minus age

Two major factors form the cardiac output, the heart rate, which is the number of times the heart beats each minute, and the **stroke volume**, which is the volume of blood that leaves the heart during each contraction.

Increasing the heart rate increases the cardiac output by increasing the number of times the stroke volume of the heart is released into the system. The stroke volume can be increased by the heart contracting with more force and so pushing more blood out with each beat. The cardiac output, heart rate and stroke volume are related such that:

cardiac output (CO) = stroke volume (SV) × heart rate (HR)

The blood that leaves the heart (the cardiac output) is under pressure in the arteries so that it can manage to reach all parts of the body. **Blood pressure** is measured in millimetres of mercury (mmHg). There are two measurements:

- **systolic pressure** – the higher blood-pressure measurement that occurs when the heart beats, pushing blood through the arteries and
- **diastolic pressure** – the lower blood-pressure measurement that occurs when the heart rests between beats.

Both systolic and diastolic blood pressures are measured and given as two values. A young, fit person should have a blood pressure of about 120 over 70, which means their systolic pressure is 120 mmHg and their diastolic pressure is 70 mmHg. The normal range for blood pressures is between 120/80 mmHg and 90/60 mmHg.

There are various factors that can increase blood pressure, including smoking, being overweight, drinking a lot of alcohol, and stress. **High blood pressure** can cause kidney damage, burst blood vessels and damage to the brain, including strokes. A typical high blood pressure is 140/90 mmHg.

Low blood pressure is often the result of a poor diet and/or a lack of exercise. Low blood pressure can cause dizziness, fainting and poor blood circulation. A typical low blood pressure is 90/60 mmHg.

Key words

Maximum heart rate (MHR): calculated as 220 – age.
Cardiac output: amount of blood leaving the heart per minute.
Stroke volume: amount of blood leaving the heart each beat.
Systolic pressure: the blood pressure in the arteries during the contraction of your heart.
Diastolic pressure: the blood pressure in the arteries when the heart rests between beats.
High blood pressure: blood pressure above 120/80.
Low blood pressure: blood pressure less than 90/60.

Activity

Work with a partner. Locate your own radial or carotid pulse and count each time you feel your pulse (it feels like a 'bump'), while your partner counts to ten seconds. Multiply this by six to work out your resting heart rate in beats per minute. Keep a note of this figure.

Now do 30 seconds of some simple exercise, such as squat thrusts or burpees, and repeat taking your pulse as soon as possible after you have finished exercising. Compare your heart rate after exercise to your resting heart rate.

Test yourself

1 What is the formula for calculating a person's maximum heart rate?
2 Define cardiac output and stroke volume.
3 Write the equation to calculate cardiac output.
4 Describe the difference between systolic and diastolic blood pressures.
5 What are the average values for blood pressure?
6 Suggest a value for high blood pressure and a value for low blood pressure.

Remember

- Arteries mainly carry oxygenated blood away from the heart.
- Veins mainly carry deoxygenated blood towards the heart; veins have valves.
- Capillaries are thin-walled to allow for gaseous exchange.
- The vascular shunt mechanism redistributes blood to where it is in demand through vasoconstriction and vasodilation.
- Atria are the upper chambers of the heart.
- Ventricles are the lower chambers of the heart.
- The right side of the heart carries deoxygenated blood. The left side carries oxygenated blood.
- The aorta and pulmonary artery carry blood away from the heart.
- The vena cava and pulmonary vein carry blood towards the heart.
- Atria collect blood; ventricles pump blood.
- Right side of heart – deoxygenated blood.
- Left side of the heart – oxygenated blood.
- Pulmonary blood vessels go to and from the lungs.
- Heart rate is the number of times the heart contracts per minute.
- Maximum heart rate is 220 – age.
- Cardiac output = stroke volume × heart rate.
- Cardiac output is the amount of blood leaving the heart per minute.
- Stroke volume is the amount of blood leaving the heart per beat.
- Blood in arteries is under pressure when the heart contracts (systolic) and when the heart is relaxed (diastolic).

Review questions

1. Suggest **three** differences between the structure of arteries and veins.
2. Suggest **two** differences between the functions of arteries and veins.
3. Describe the main functions of capillaries.
4. Explain the difference between vasoconstriction and vasodilation.
5. Name the heart chamber that receives blood from the vena cava.
6. Name the heart chamber that sends blood to the aorta.
7. Name the two blood vessels that carry deoxygenated blood to/from the heart.
8. Name the two blood vessels that carry oxygenated blood to/from the heart.
9. Describe the route taken by deoxygenated blood from when it enters the heart until it becomes oxygenated.
10. Describe the route taken by oxygenated blood from when it enters the heart until it leaves the heart.
11. Calculate the maximum heart rate of a 24-year-old person.
12. Define the terms 'cardiac output' and 'stroke volume' and state the relationship between them.
13. Suggest average values for systolic and diastolic blood pressures.

1.5 Energy systems

When you exercise you need to supply energy for muscle contractions. This energy is usually supplied by breaking down food (mainly glucose) using oxygen. Because this process uses oxygen it is called the **aerobic energy system**.

The aerobic energy system is used at low to moderate levels of exertion, when energy can be produced using oxygen. Walking, jogging and resting are good examples of activities where the energy for muscle contractions is provided aerobically. The process may be summarised as:

glucose + oxygen → energy + carbon dioxide + water

You can see from the equation that glucose is broken down using oxygen to provide energy, with water and carbon dioxide produced as waste products.

Figure 1.61 Jogging is an aerobic exercise.

The **anaerobic energy system** is used when the energy needed for exercise is provided without being dependent on oxygen. The anaerobic energy system is used for activities lasting less than a minute and **lactic acid** is produced as a waste product. Sprinting, jumping and shot-putting are examples of activities where the energy is provided anaerobically.

In the anaerobic energy system, no oxygen is used. Because of this, the glucose is not fully broken down to carbon dioxide and water. Instead it is converted into lactic acid while producing the energy needed for the activity. The process may be summarised as:

glucose → energy + lactic acid

Key words

Aerobic energy system: uses/is dependent on oxygen; used for long-duration, low-intensity activities.

Anaerobic energy system: not dependent on oxygen used for short duration; used for high-intensity activities.

Lactic acid: fatiguing waste product of the anaerobic energy system.

Figure 1.62 Exercise may cause fatigue.

Lactic acid is a major cause of fatigue. This is why activities involving the anaerobic energy system cannot be continued for more than a minute or so. The build-up of lactic acid in muscles causes fatigue and eventually pain, and the exercise has to slow down or, if strenuous, stop.

The main difference between exercises using the aerobic and anaerobic energy systems is the intensity and the duration of the exercise involved.

Aerobic activities involve relatively gentle exercises that can be maintained for over a minute, and often much longer. Aerobic activities are those where normal breathing can be used to supply the oxygen needed to the working muscles.

Anaerobic activities involve very high-intensity movements that can only be continued for a short period of time. Anaerobic exercises, if continued, will leave you breathless.

Figure 1.63 Sprinting is an anaerobic exercise.

There are some activities, such as team games, that contain a mixture of aerobic and anaerobic exercise. During team games there will be times when the exercise is relatively gentle – when the performer is walking or jogging – and is aerobic. At other times the performer may be sprinting, and the exercise is strenuous and becomes anaerobic.

Figure 1.64 Team games involve a mixture of aerobic and anaerobic exercise.

Activity

Copy and complete the table by ticking in the appropriate box whether the activity is mainly aerobic, anaerobic or a mixture of both energy systems.

Activity	Aerobic	Anaerobic	Mixture of both
100 m sprint			
Marathon running			
Pole vault			
Hockey match			
Trampolining sequence			
Rugby tackle			

Activity

Copy and complete the table by listing the advantages and disadvantages of using the aerobic and anaerobic energy systems during exercise.

	Aerobic energy system	Anaerobic energy system
Advantages		
Disadvantages		

Test yourself

1   Write an equation to summarise the aerobic energy system.
2   Write an equation to summarise the anaerobic energy system.
3   Describe the effects of lactic acid on the body.
4   Name activities that are mainly aerobic or mainly anaerobic.

Activity

Using an example of a named team game, identify those aspects of the team game that use the aerobic energy system and the anaerobic energy system.

Remember

- The aerobic energy system is used in long-duration, low-intensity exercises.
- The anaerobic energy system is used in short-duration, high-intensity exercises.
- The aerobic energy system uses oxygen to break down glucose to release energy and produces water and carbon dioxide as waste products.
- The anaerobic energy system does not need oxygen to break down glucose to release energy and produces lactic acid as a waste product.
- Lactic acid causes fatigue.

Review questions

1   Write an equation to summarise the aerobic energy system.
2   Suggest **two** differences between the aerobic and anaerobic energy systems.
3   Give **two** examples of activities from a team game using the aerobic energy system and **two** examples of activities from the same team game using the anaerobic energy system.

Learning outcome 2: understand the effects of health and fitness activities on the body

In this learning outcome you will be shown:

- the short-term effects of health and fitness activities on the body, including:
  - breathing rate
  - heart rate, stroke volume and cardiac output
  - blood pressure
  - body temperature
  - sweating
  - hydration levels
  - muscle fatigue
  - delayed onset of muscle soreness (DOMS)
- the long-term effects of health and fitness activities on the body, including:
  - cardiovascular endurance
  - efficiency to use oxygen
  - blood pressure
  - resting heart rate
  - muscular endurance
  - muscular strength
  - muscle hypertrophy
  - red blood cells
  - flexibility
  - body shape (endomorph, ectomorph, mesomorph).

2.1 Effects of health and fitness activities on the body

2.1.1 Short-term effects of health and fitness activities

Athletes and performers will experience differing short-term effects on the body depending on what exercise type they are taking part in. When a performer starts to exercise, the intensity and type of exercise will determine what immediate effects the body experiences. However, performers tend to:

- get hot and sweaty
- get red skin as the blood is shunted towards the surface
- have an increase in the depth and frequency of breathing
- experience an increase in heart rate.

In this book, we will classify short-term as being anything up to 36 hours after the start of exercise. The main short-term effects are explained in Table 1.3.

> **Key word**
>
> **DOMS**: delayed onset of muscle soreness.

Table 1.3 Short-term effects of exercise

Short-term effect	Explanation
Breathing rate increases	As the body's muscles need more oxygen to make energy, breathing rate increases.
Heart rate increases	Heart rate increases to force blood to get to the muscles quicker – carrying oxygen.
Stroke volume increases	Stroke volume is the amount of blood ejected from the heart ventricles per beat (contraction). This increases during exercise to pump more blood out.
Cardiac output	Cardiac output is the volume of blood pumped out by the heart per minute. As discussed in Section 1.4.4, it is calculated as stroke volume (SV) × heart rate (HR). As heart rate and stroke volume increase during exercise, so does cardiac output.
Blood pressure increases	During exercise it is important to increase the flow of blood to muscles to provide them with oxygen. As blood pressure increases, the heart forces blood out of the ventricles with more pressure.
Body temperature increases	Up to 70% of the energy that powers muscles during exercise is lost as heat. This heat has to be lost by the body and blood is pushed closer to the skin to do this.
Hydration levels decrease	As the body starts to sweat, body fluid is lost and hydration levels decrease. This can cause dehydration, whereby the blood becomes thick (viscous) and decision-making is negatively affected. Heart rate will also rise to keep the viscous blood flowing.
Muscle fatigue occurs	As the muscles start to build up lactic acid, muscle function can be negatively affected and fatigue occurs.
Delayed onset of muscle soreness (**DOMS**) occurs	The delayed onset of muscle soreness (DOMS) tends to occur 24–48 hours after exercise. This is caused by small tears in the muscle fibres as a result of exercise.

Figure 1.65 Sweating during exercise causes the body to lose fluid.

Remember that exercise immediately makes you feel SAD (not literally!):

- **S**weaty
- **A**ccelerated heart rate
- **D**epth of breathing increases.

Test yourself

1 State two immediate effects of exercise.
2 State two possible short-term effects of a period of exercise.
3 Why might a performer who has run a marathon have red skin and sore muscles?

2.1.2 Long-term effects of health and fitness activities

Athletes and performers will experience differing long-term effects on the body depending on what exercise type they have taken part in.

After months and/or years of exercise the body adapts to what it has been doing. Three examples are given in the table.

Table 1.4 How the body adapts to different types of exercise

Long-term cardiovascular/aerobic light-intensity training	Weight training using light weights and high reps	Weight training using heavy weights and low reps
• body shape may change (e.g. more muscle tone) • improvements in specific components of fitness (e.g. cardiovascular endurance) • improved muscular endurance • improved stamina (being able to withstand fatigue) • increase in the size of the heart (**hypertrophy**) • lower blood pressure (as exercise increases the size of your heart, more blood can be pumped out per beat) • lower resting heart rate (**bradycardia**) • improved ability to use oxygen • more **red blood cells** made	• body shape may change (e.g. more muscle tone, slightly more **mesomorph** characteristics) • improvements in specific components of fitness (e.g. muscular endurance) • slight increase in the size of the heart (hypertrophy) • slightly lower resting heart rate (bradycardia)	• body shape may change (e.g. more muscle bulk/size [hypertrophy], more mesomorph characteristics) • improvements in specific components of fitness (e.g. muscle strength/power)

Key words

Hypertrophy: increase in size due to training (e.g. hypertrophy of the left ventricle in the heart).
Bradycardia: lower resting heart rate as a result of training.
Red blood cell: carries oxygen in the blood.
Mesomorph: body shape characterised by large muscular shoulders.
Ectomorph: body shape characterised by lean, skinny, low muscle mass. Ectomorphs are often tall.

Long-term changes are generally characterised by what the person has been doing. For example:

• lots of stretching results in an increase in flexibility
• lots of endurance work results in a greater ability to use oxygen.

However, training can also affect a person's body shape. If a person increases muscle mass they become more of a mesomorph, whereas as a person loses weight, they become more of an **ectomorph**. There are three distinctive body shapes, which are shown in Figure 1.66.

Key word

Endomorph: body shape characterised by large fat content.

Ectomorph   Mesomorph   Endomorph

Figure 1.66 Different body shapes

Activity

On a piece of paper draw a simple sketch to show an extreme mesomorph, endomorph and ectomorph.

Remember the long-term effects of endurance training by using STEAM:

- **S**ize of the heart increases
- **T**one of the muscles is more pronounced
- **E**ndurance improves (cardiovascular)
- **A**ble to better withstand fatigue
- **M**uscular endurance also improves.

Activity

Write down the following phrases and try to link them to what a performer may have been doing for these long-term changes to have occurred:

more muscle mass, improved muscular endurance, lower resting heart rate, bigger heart muscle.

Read about it

Watch the following YouTube clips about the long-term effects of exercise on the body.

www.tinyurl.com/yazn9n3y

www.tinyurl.com/yc5wggcq

Test yourself

1 State three long-term effects of endurance training.
2 If a performer lifted light weights when training over a period of several months, what adaptations would occur to their body?
3 How do you increase flexibility?

Remember

- An increase in heart rate and the depth of breathing are immediate effects of exercise.
- Short-term effects of exercise include increased body temperature, muscle fatigue and DOMS.
- Cardiac output increases during exercise. It is stroke volume × heart rate.
- Long-term effects of exercise depend on what type of training you have done. For example, endurance training results in a larger heart muscle (hypertrophy) and lower resting heart rate.
- Heavy weight training results in hypertrophy of the muscles and greater strength. This causes the body to look more like that of a mesomorph.
- Training with light weights results in muscle tone.
- Different body shapes can be characterised by the names mesomorph, ectomorph and endomorph.

Assessment practice

1 Describe what happens to heart rate and breathing rate as a result of starting to perform exercise.
2 Describe a mesomorph body shape.
3 State three effects of long-term endurance training.
4 State four immediate effects of starting to exercise.
5 Describe what happens to cardiac output during exercise.
6 What is meant by the term 'stroke volume'?
7 What is meant by the term 'cardiac output'?
8 What is DOMS and when would it occur?
9 What is meant by the term 'bradycardia' and why might it happen?

Learning outcome 3: understand health and fitness and the components of fitness

In this learning outcome you will be shown:

- what the terms health and fitness mean
- the components of fitness and how they apply to health and fitness activities
- the components of health-related fitness including:
  - cardiovascular endurance
  - muscular strength – static, dynamic and explosive
  - muscular endurance
  - body composition
  - flexibility
- the components of skill-related fitness including:
  - agility
  - speed
  - co-ordination
  - power
  - balance
  - reaction time.

3.1 Health and fitness

Health includes three distinctive factors, which must all be present for a person to be deemed 'healthy': mental, physical and social (health and wellbeing). It is defined by the World Health Organisation (WHO) (1948) as 'a state of complete physical, mental and social wellbeing and not merely the absence of disease or infirmity'. It is therefore important that you understand the different components of being 'healthy' (see Figure 1.67.)

Fitness is defined as the ability to cope with daily demands without suffering undue fatigue. In other words, your body is fit enough to do what it needs to do. Clearly as a person gets fitter, they can cope with daily demands more easily.

Key words

Health: 'a state of complete physical, mental and social wellbeing and not merely the absence of disease or infirmity' (WHO, 1948).
Fitness: the ability to cope with daily demands without suffering undue fatigue. In other words, your body is fit enough to do what it needs to do.

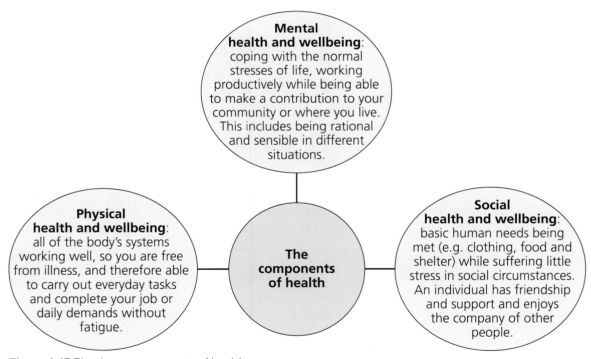

Figure 1.67 The three components of health

The relationship between health and fitness

Fitness and health do not necessarily relate to or guarantee each other. Being 'fit' forms part of your physical health but may not mean you are mentally healthy. Different scenarios and relationship issues between health and fitness include:

- Having a high level of fitness does not necessarily mean you are healthy – you can be physically fit, but have poor social health, for example.
- Being of poor health can result in an inability to train, which would lower fitness levels.
- If an individual has poor mental health, this may result in overtraining to try to achieve higher levels of fitness.
- If a person is fit, it does not mean that they definitely like to socialise (social health).
- It is possible to be unhealthy (e.g. suffer from a mental illness) but be able to train, and therefore increase fitness.

Figure 1.68 To be 'healthy' is to be physically, socially and mentally well.

Activity

List the daily demands that you have in your life. Tick which ones you feel you can cope with (without undue fatigue) and therefore have a suitable level of fitness.

Test yourself

1 State the three components of health.
2 Describe the relationship between health and fitness.
3 'If you train a lot to get fitter it will improve your health' – is this correct?

3.2 Components of fitness

The different components of fitness are categorised as either health-related or skill-related.

3.2.1 Health-related fitness

There are five components of health-related fitness. It is important that you can link these components to health and fitness activities and understand the effect that improvements to the component(s) have on performance in the activity. The basic definitions of these five components of health-related fitness are shown in Table 1.5.

Table 1.5 The five components of health-related fitness

Component	Definition
Cardiovascular endurance	the ability of the heart and lungs to supply oxygen to the working muscles
Flexibility	the range of movement possible at a joint
Muscular endurance	the ability of a muscle or muscle group to undergo repeated contractions avoiding fatigue
Muscular strength	the ability to overcome a resistance There are three types of strength: ● static – maximal strength that can be applied to an immoveable object ● dynamic – repeated contractions applied to a moving object ● explosive – sometimes called power. A combination of strength × speed
Body composition	a comparison of the percentages of bone, fat, water and muscle within the body

Key words

Cardiovascular endurance: the ability of the heart and lungs to supply oxygen to the working muscles.

Flexibility: the range of movement possible at a joint.

Muscular endurance: the ability of a muscle or muscle group to undergo repeated contractions avoiding fatigue.

Muscular strength: the ability to overcome a resistance.

Body composition: a comparison of the percentages of bone, fat, water and muscle within the body.

As well as knowing the definitions, you need to understand when these components are needed and how improvement could benefit performance. Table 1.6 provides some examples.

Table 1.6 When the five components of health-related fitness are used

Component	Physical activity
Cardiovascular endurance	Used by marathon runners to keep the body working aerobically during the whole event
Flexibility	Used by gymnasts to perform specific moves which require a range of movement (e.g. splits)
Muscular endurance	Used by badminton players to keep moving round the court for a whole game
Muscular strength	Static strength is used by rugby players in a scrum Dynamic strength is used by rowers to repeated moving the oar with force throughout a 2000 m race
Body composition	Certain body compositions may provide advantages (e.g. it may be better for a high jumper to be tall and thin)

Figure 1.69 Marathon running requires a high level of cardiovascular endurance.

Activity

Using the examples in Table 1.6, try to come up with more examples from other sports of when each of the components of fitness could provide an advantage.

Test yourself

1 What is cardiovascular endurance?
2 Give examples of skills from sports that require flexibility or static strength.
3 State three health-related components of fitness required when playing a team game like football.

3.2.2 Skill-related fitness

There are six components of skill-related fitness. It is important that you can link these components to health and fitness activities and understand the effect that improvements to the component(s) have on performance in the activity. The basic definitions of these six components of health-related fitness are shown in Table 1.7.

Table 1.7 The six components of skill-related fitness are used

Component	Definition
Agility	the ability to move and change directly quickly (at speed) while maintaining control
Balance	the maintenance of the centre of mass over the base of support
Co-ordination	the ability to use different (two or more) parts of the body together smoothly and efficiently
Power	explosive strength or anaerobic power is the product of strength and speed (i.e. strength × speed)
Reaction time	the time taken to initiate a response to a stimulus
Speed	the maximum rate at which an individual is able to perform a movement or cover a distance in a period of time. It is also defined as putting the body parts into action as quickly as possible

You can remember the components of skill-related fitness by using the acronym PCRABS:

- **P**ower
- **C**o-ordination
- **R**eaction time
- **A**gility
- **B**alance
- **S**peed.

Key words

Power: explosive strength or anaerobic power is the product of strength and speed: i.e. strength × speed.

Co-ordination: the ability to use different (two or more) parts of the body together smoothly and efficiently.

Reaction time: the time taken to initiate a response to a stimulus.
Agility: the ability to move and change direction quickly (at speed) while maintaining control.

Balance: the maintenance of the centre of mass over the base of support.

Speed: the maximum rate at which an individual is able to perform a movement or cover a distance in a period of time. It is also defined as putting the body parts into action as quickly as possible.

Activity

Using Table 1.8, try to come up with more examples from other sports of when each of the components of fitness could provide an advantage.

As well as knowing the definitions, you need to understand when these components are needed and how improvement could benefit performance.

Table 1.8 provides some examples.

Table 1.8 When the six components of skill-related fitness are used

Component	Physical activity
Agility	Needed in badminton to change direction at speed when intercepting an opponent's shot
Balance	Needed to hold a handstand position in gymnastics
Co-ordination	Needed to move feet and swing a racket to hit a tennis ball
Power	Needed to punch with force in boxing
Reaction time	Needed to react to the stimulus of a gun in a 100 m race
Speed	Needed to sprint for 200 m

Figure 1.70 Basketball requires agility to change direction at speed when dribbling.

Test yourself

1 What is agility?
2 How could developing speed help you in netball?
3 Give an example of a stimulus and a reaction required in a sport of your choice.
4 What two body parts need to be 'co-ordinated' to catch a ball?

Activity

Create a set of top trumps using a variety of activities, to give each activity a score for each of the 11 components (health- and skill-related) according to the relative importance of each component to that activity.

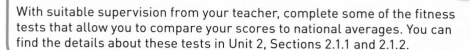

Activity

With suitable supervision from your teacher, complete some of the fitness tests that allow you to compare your scores to national averages. You can find the details about these tests in Unit 2, Sections 2.1.1 and 2.1.2.

Remember

- Health is defined as 'a state of complete physical, mental and social wellbeing and not merely the absence of disease or infirmity'.
- Fitness is defined as 'the ability to cope with daily demands without suffering undue fatigue'.
- Health does not necessarily mean you are fit, and vice versa.
- You could have a high level of fitness but a poor state of mental health.
- The components of fitness are split into health-related and skill-related.
- The health-related components of fitness are cardiovascular endurance, flexibility, muscular endurance, strength, and body composition.
- The skill-related components of fitness are co-ordination, reaction time, agility, balance, speed and power.
- Each component of fitness can be related to improved performance (e.g. improved speed would benefit a 100 m sprinter).

Review questions

1. Define the term 'health'.
2. State the six skill-related components of fitness.
3. Suggest two skill-related fitness components needed by a boxer, justifying your choices.
4. Why is co-ordination needed to play badminton?
5. What is cardiovascular endurance?
6. State the five health-related components of fitness.
7. Define body composition.
8. Why is cardiovascular endurance needed for a team-sports player (for example, rugby or netball)?

Learning outcome 4: understand the principles of training

In this learning outcome you will be shown:

- the five principles of training and how they can be applied to health and fitness activities
- the principles of FITT and how they can be adapted to optimise performance in health and fitness activities.

4.1 Principles of training

4.1.1 The principles of training

The principles of training act as a guide and should be considered for all prolonged periods of training. The principles are often remembered as SPORT:

- **S**pecificity
- **P**rogression
- **O**verload
- **R**eversibility
- **T**edium

Specificity refers to the fact that training should be specific to the needs of an individual and the demands of the sport that they take part in. For instance, a sprinter would be likely to do more anaerobic, speed and power work because these are the important needs for that activity.

Any training done should be specific to the muscles used and the energy demands of the activity. Cyclists, for example, would not lift heavy weights to strengthen their arms, as strong arms are not needed for cycling. Cyclists need strength in their legs, as their legs are the specific body part that do most of the work.

Although **progression** and **overload** are often discussed separately, they can also be grouped together. Overload is simply 'working harder than normal'. If you do this, the body will adapt to the stresses being put upon it and will gradually improve. However, progression refers to the fact that the overload should gradually be increased as the body adapts and gets better. The progressive overload on the body may mean gradually running further or faster, lifting heavier weights, or lifting similar weights more often. Training should overload the body gradually, because if it progresses too quickly, then an individual may suffer an injury.

> **Key words**
>
> **Specificity**: training must be relevant for your chosen activity.
>
> **Progression**: gradually increasing the intensity of training.
>
> **Overload**: working harder than normal.

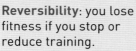
Reversibility simply states that if an individual stops or reduces their training level, then fitness and performance are likely to drop. Muscle strength and cardiovascular endurance can drop quite quickly if training is stopped altogether.

Tedium refers to boredom. Simply repeating the same sort of training, every time you train, quickly becomes boring. Training should be altered and varied to prevent an individual from suffering from this.

For example, a rugby circuit-training programme would use the principles of training by including:

- Specificity – circuits would focus on the specific muscles used, the energy systems used, the movements used and the fitness components needed in rugby.
- Progressive overload – when the circuit training is repeated, it would gradually be made harder by doing the circuit more often, by making the individual do more exercises, by increasing how long they are exercising for, or by reducing the amount of rest they get between exercises.
- Reversibility – the circuit training would be repeated regularly to prevent loss of fitness.
- Tedium – the exercises used in the circuit training would be varied to prevent boredom, for example, shuttle runs, press-ups, sit-ups, vertical jumps/squats, quick rugby passes, etc. (all relevant to rugby).

Key words

Reversibility: you lose fitness if you stop or reduce training.

Tedium: training needs to be varied to avoid boredom.

Activity

Copy and complete the table by adding the correct definition of each of the terms and an example of how to use that principle from a sport of your choice.

Principle	Definition	Example of using the principle
Specificity		
Progression		
Overload		
Reversibility		
Tedium		

Test yourself

1. List the five principles of training.
2. Describe each of the principles of training.
3. Describe the effects of lactic acid on the body.
4. Name activities that are mainly aerobic and/or mainly anaerobic.

4.1.2 Principles of FITT

Overload is one of the principles of training. Overload is working harder than normal. There are four ways of working harder, and these are the principles of FITT. These principles are particularly important for exercise at a low to medium intensity.

In the principles of FITT, F stands for frequency, I stands for intensity, T stands for time, T also stands for type.

These four guidelines should be used when deciding the amount of overload to be used within a training programme. The details of FITT include:

- **Frequency** – refers to how often someone trains. Normally training should take place three or more times a week. As fitness increases, the ability to train more often also becomes possible.
- **Intensity** – refers to how hard you train: how fast you run/how heavy the weights are that you are lifting, etc. As fitness increases, the intensity of the exercises should be suitably increased.
- **Time** – refers to how long you train for. As fitness increases, the length of time spent training should increase.
- **Type** – refers to the type of training used (for example, continuous training, circuit training or weight training). The type of training must remain suitable to gain the specific fitness benefits that are required.

The example of circuit training for rugby used in the previous section, would incorporate the principles of FITT training in that:

- The frequency of training could be increased to incorporate overload. For example, training could be done more often – three times a week instead of two.
- The intensity of the circuit training could be increased by training harder. This could be done by doing more exercises, or doing each exercise for longer, or making each exercise slightly harder, or allowing a shorter rest between exercises.
- The time taken to train could be increased, for example, by doing the circuit training for 30 instead of 20 minutes.
- The type of training could be changed, for example, instead of the usual circuit training, some passing or kicking drills could be added as part of the circuit, or a short game of touch rugby could be played.

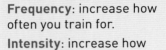

Key words

Frequency: increase how often you train for.

Intensity: increase how much training is done.

Time: increase the duration of your training.

Type: vary the type of training.

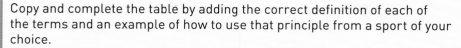
Activity

Copy and complete the table by adding the correct definition of each of the terms and an example of how to use that principle from a sport of your choice.

Principle	Definition	Example of using the principle
Frequency		
Intensity		
Time		
Type		

Activity

Copy out the example below of a training programme for a football midfield player.

Identify and highlight how the principles of SPORT and FITT have been used in this programme by using one colour for SPORT and another colour for FITT. Which principles have not been used?

Week 1	Programme – focus on cardiovascular endurance
Monday	Did 20 minutes jogging at a steady pace
Tuesday	Rest day
Wednesday	Went swimming – managed six lengths but got bored and stopped
Thursday	Rest day because of aching muscles
Friday	Went for a ten-minute jog, which included some hills, but got too tired so stopped
Saturday	Wanted to try cycling instead of jogging, but bike had puncture
Sunday	Rest day

Test yourself

1 Name the FITT principles.
2 Explain the FITT principles.
3 Give examples of the use of the FITT principles for a sport of your choice.

Remember

- Training needs to be specific to the activity you are training for.
- Training needs to get gradually harder as fitness improves.
- The benefits of training are soon lost if you stop or reduce training.
- Training needs to be varied because repeating the same training sessions over and over again becomes boring.
- Use the FITT principles to overload.
- Gradually increase the frequency of training by training more often.
- Gradually increase the intensity of training by training harder.
- Gradually increase the amount of time you train for.
- Vary the type of training you do.

Review questions

1 Name the **five** training principles.
2 Explain the training principle of specificity.
3 Suggest how the training principles of overload and progression could be applied to a marathon runner.
4 Identify the four FITT principles of overload.
5 Suggest how you could apply the FITT principle of intensity to a training programme.

Unit 2 Preparing and planning for health and fitness

About this unit

In this unit you will:

- develop knowledge and understanding of how to prepare and plan for health and fitness
- understand the impact of lifestyle on health and fitness and be able to apply health and fitness analyses to set goals
- develop knowledge and understanding of how to test and develop components of fitness
- develop knowledge and understanding of how to structure a health and fitness programme and how to prepare safely for health and fitness activities.

Learning outcomes

The unit is divided into four learning outcomes:

- **LO1**: The learner will understand the impact of lifestyle on health and fitness.
- **LO2**: The learner will understand how to test and develop components of fitness.
- **LO3**: The learner will understand how to apply health and fitness analyses and set goals.
- **LO4**: The learner will understand the structure of a health and fitness programme and how to prepare safely.

How will I be assessed?

The assessment for this unit will be internally assessed via a synoptic project.

Learning outcome 1: understand the impact of lifestyle on health and fitness

In this learning outcome you will develop knowledge and understanding of the impact of lifestyle on health and fitness, including:

- activity levels
- diet
- rest and recovery
- factors such as drugs, smoking, alcohol and stress.

1.1 Lifestyle factors

1.1.1 Activity levels

A person's **lifestyle** involves a series of choices. For example, a person's lifestyle can be active, healthy, sociable; or the complete opposite – inactive, unhealthy and unsociable. It is a person's choice how they lead their life.

There are of course many factors that could affect a person's lifestyle choices. Some of these are suggested below:

- disposable income
- where you live
- family, friends and their lifestyles
- opportunities and facilities
- education levels.

If a person decides to adopt a lifestyle that involves little or no exercise, this is known as a '**sedentary lifestyle**'. A person who a sedentary lifestyle increases the chances of developing illness and/or poor health and wellbeing.

The National Health Service (NHS) plays a proactive part in attempting to encourage an **active lifestyle** and actually sets suggested exercise rates. These can be found at: **www.tinyurl.com/y7dlenh8**

There is also a factsheet available on the NHS website at: **www.tinyurl.com/y6uc9us4**

NHS guidelines state that 'to stay healthy or improve health, adults need to do two types of physical activity each week':

- moderate aerobic exercise, or vigorous exercise
  and
- strength exercises.

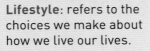

Key words

Lifestyle: refers to the choices we make about how we live our lives.

Sedentary lifestyle: refers to a person's choice to have little or no exercise.

Active lifestyle: a lifestyle in which the person chooses to include suitable levels of exercise.

The amount of moderate aerobic exercise and strength exercise you need to do depends entirely upon your age.

Examples of moderate aerobic exercise include:

● brisk walking
● hiking
● pushing a lawn mower
● playing team sports recreationally
● skateboarding.

Examples of strength exercises include:

● lifting weights
● use of resistance bands
● heavy gardening
● using your own body weight – for example, sit-ups/press-ups.

NHS guidelines also suggest that vigorous exercise, which makes you work harder and breathe faster, may have even more health benefits than moderate aerobic exercise. Examples include: swimming fast, running, martial arts or playing a team sport. The benefits may be twice as useful as moderate aerobic exercise – one example of an NHS initiative towards planning a vigorous workout is called 'Couch to 5k'.

All NHS guidelines are based on four different age ranges:

● early childhood (under 5 years old)
● young people (5–18 years old)
● adults (19–64 years old)
● older adults (65 and over).

For adults aged 19–64 years, there are several suggested variations of exercise for a suitable active lifestyle. These are shown in Figure 2.1.

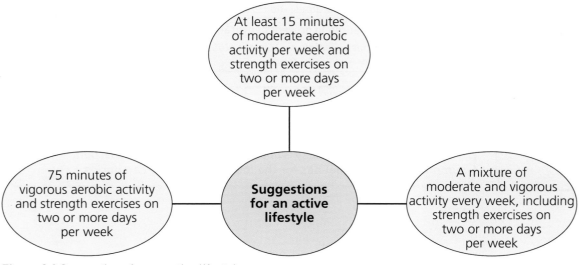

Figure 2.1 Suggestions for an active lifestyle

1.1.2 Diet

Nutrients

A nutrient is a substance that is essential for our bodies to grow, repair and work properly.

A breakdown of what each nutrient contributes within the body, is shown in Table 2.1. The table also shows suitable food sources of each nutrient.

Table 2.1 Nutrients and their contributions

Nutrient	Specific need
Carbohydrates	The main and preferred energy source for all types of activity
	Required for high- and low-intensity energy
	Works as a fuel for muscular contractions, acting as the main fuel for medium- to high-intensity exercise (80% + anaerobic activity)
	Particularly useful for one minute to two hours of exercise
	Provided within bread, pasta, potatoes and starch-based foodstuffs
Fats	Also an energy source
	Required for low-intensity energy (aerobic, at 60% or less- of maximal heart rate) and insulation
	Comes in two forms:
	● saturated fat (usually animal fat)
	● unsaturated fat (vegetable fat/oils)
	(NB: Saturated fat can be responsible for clogging arteries.)
Protein	Required for tissue growth and repair
	Has a small part to play in energy
	Provided by foodstuffs like fish, meat eggs, dairy products and nuts
Minerals	Required for bone growth and the maintenance of regular body functions
	Inorganic substances (e.g. calcium is good for bone formation)
Fibre	Required to reduce cholesterol and helps to soften stool to prevent constipation
	Found in foods that come from plants (e.g. oats, barley, wholemeal bread, potatoes and cereals)
Water	Required to prevent dehydration
	Approximately six to eight glasses should be drunk in an average day – around 1.2 litres

Read about it

Read about the importance of fibre in the diet: **www.tinyurl.com/yd7sq98k**

Activity

Log in to the NHS website and study the information located at **www.tinyurl.com/y7dlenh8**. Make a poster to display in your classroom summarising the guidelines for the four different age categories.

Balanced diet

A **balanced diet** is one where all of the nutrients are obtained in the correct quantities from a range of different foodstuff. To have a truly 'balanced diet' the body should consume approximately:

- 55–60 per cent carbohydrates
- 25–30 per cent fat
- 15–20 per cent protein.

One aspect of a balanced diet means that people are consuming a suitable number of calories to satisfy their energy demands. The 'energy balance' refers to the relationship between the amount consumed and the amount required. The amount consumed can result in the following outcomes:

- Energy is balanced: this means that the amount consumed equals the amount needed and no weight is put on or lost.
- Positive energy balance: this means that the amount consumed is greater than what is needed, resulting in weight gain.
- Negative energy balance: this means that the amount consumed is less than what is needed, resulting in weight loss.

The required energy intake depends upon whether you are a man or a woman, and what kind of lifestyle you lead. For example, a job that requires manual labour (such as a builder) will require more energy, whereas a sedentary office job requires less.

Similarly, suitable nutrition and a balanced diet can be different for different types of physical activity. For example:

- Carbohydrates are consumed in larger quantities than normal before endurance events like a long run so that they do not run out during the event. This is called carbohydrate loading.
- Protein is consumed after exercise to assist in muscle repair (for example, after a training workout).
- Water will need to be consumed in greater quantities for people doing exercise or with a more active lifestyle.

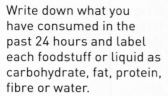

Activity

Write down what you have consumed in the past 24 hours and label each foodstuff or liquid as carbohydrate, fat, protein, fibre or water.

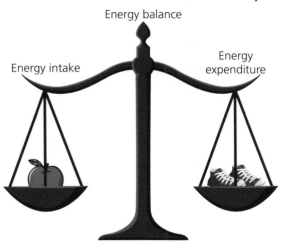

Figure 2.2 Energy balance refers to the balance between what you consume (calories) to what you use.

Activity

Weigh out how much food you think is in a recommended portion and then weigh out the actual recommended portion size and compare the differences. You could also discuss how this portion size may change based on different factors or goals.

Use this link to help you: www.tinyurl.com/y7fkp6ht

Balanced diet guidance

It is important to include all of the nutrients in a diet. You need to know how to provide advice on dietary changes. A good starting point is the 'Eatwell Guide', published by Public Health England. This guide recommends that all

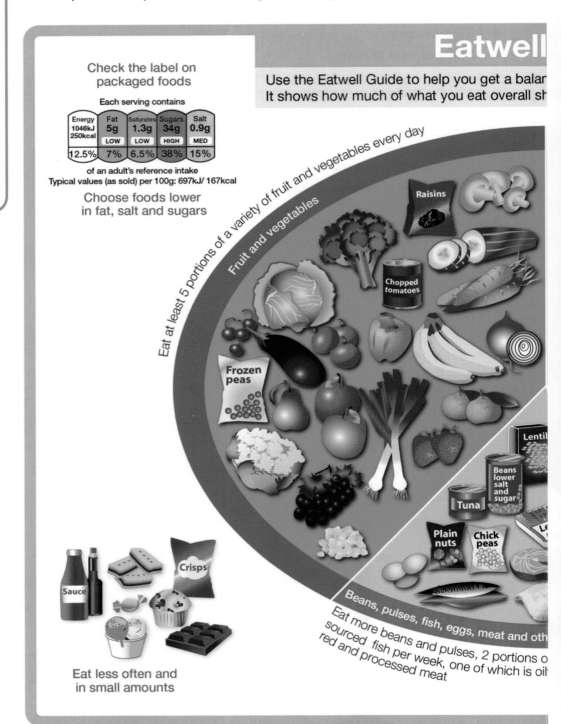

Source: Public Health England in association with the Welsh government, Food Standards Scotland and the Food Standards Agency in Northern Ireland

Figure 2.3 The Eatwell Guide

adults eat at least five portions of fruit and vegetables a day, two portions of oily fish a week, and that starchy carbohydrates make up around one-third of daily intake. It also recommends that treats such as chocolate and sweets are eaten in very small amounts.

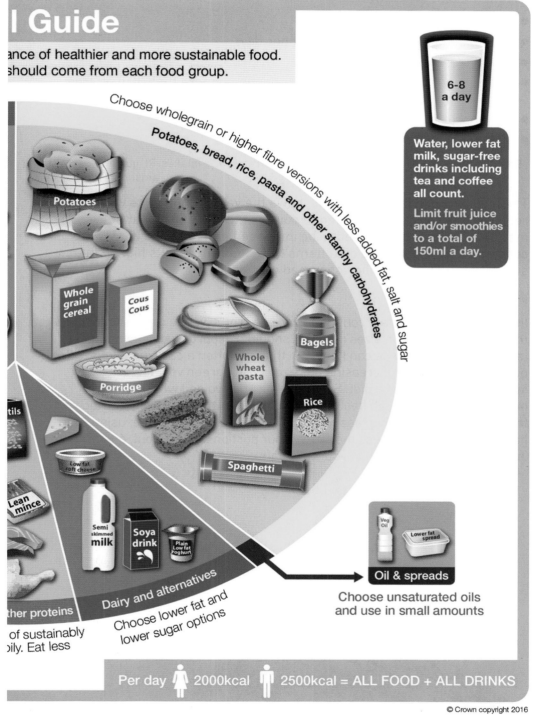

l Guide

ance of healthier and more sustainable food. should come from each food group.

Choose wholegrain or higher fibre versions with less added fat, salt and sugar

Potatoes, bread, rice, pasta and other starchy carbohydrates

Potatoes

Whole grain cereal

Cous Cous

Bagels

Whole wheat pasta

Porridge

Rice

Low fat soft cheese

Spaghetti

Lean mince

Semi skimmed milk

Soya drink

Plain Low fat yoghurt

tils

ther proteins

of sustainably ily. Eat less

Dairy and alternatives

Choose lower fat and lower sugar options

6-8 a day

Water, lower fat milk, sugar-free drinks including tea and coffee all count.

Limit fruit juice and/or smoothies to a total of 150ml a day.

Veg Oil

Lower fat spread

Oil & spreads

Choose unsaturated oils and use in small amounts

Per day 👩 2000kcal 👨 2500kcal = ALL FOOD + ALL DRINKS

© Crown copyright 2016

The Eatwell Guide also states that average adult males should consume approximately 2500 **kcal** per day and adult females 2000 kcal per day. This is known as your **recommended daily allowance** or RDA. As a term, the recommended daily allowance also refers to the recommended amount of nutrients the body needs. An average adult (19–64 years old) is recommended to:

- eat less than 70 g of fat per day
- eat less than 20 g of saturated fat per day
- eat at least 260 g of carbohydrate
- eat no more than 90 g of sugars (although no more than 30 g of 'free sugars' included in sweets, fizzy drinks, etc.)
- eat approximately 50 g of protein
- eat less than 6 g of salt.

Source: www.nhs.uk/Livewell/Goodfood/Pages/reference-intakes-RI-guideline-daily-amounts-GDA.aspx

The food pyramid (see figure 2.4) shows the varying nutrients which are required in a diet. It can be used to point out to someone what nutrients may be lacking or might need to be increased or decreased in order to consume a truly balanced diet. Items like foods and drinks high in fat, sugar or salt should not be consumed every day.

Portion size

In order to change dietary routines, there are some very simple suggestions that often help. Portion sizes in meals should be appropriate and not too large. The Eatwell Guide can help with this. It is often a case of cutting portion sizes down or increasing the size of leafy green vegetables to improve the balance of a diet. Snacks should be avoided where possible between meals, although healthy snacks (such as nuts) can help to stop you feeling hungry and eating less suitable foods. As a simple guide, using your hand can be a way to check the size of your portions. Simply put, one portion is the amount you can fit into your own palm.

Figure 2.4 The food pyramid

Eating habits

One way to control energy balance is to stick to a certain habit of eating. By habit, we mean what is normal to you in an average day. Weight gain is often the result of irregular eating patterns, particularly at night. It is generally accepted that certain practices should be followed to enable your body to function normally without excessive weight gain:

- Eat a healthy, but substantial breakfast to give the body the energy-boost it requires for the day ahead.
- Avoid late night snacks, as the potential energy consumed will not be wholly used during sleeping hours, so will be converted to stored fat.
- Aim to eat mini-meals regularly rather than huge portions in one go. This allows the body to sensibly 'top-up' regularly during the day without feeling bloated or having the psychological worry about over-indulging.
- Aim to balance your nutrient intake during the day, with all main meals featuring carbohydrates, protein, fat, fibre, vitamins and minerals and water.
- Snacking is fine as long as it is healthy – nuts are a good example of a high source of protein deemed healthy to snack on.

Test yourself

1. What are carbohydrates for?
2. What is fat for?
3. What is protein for?
4. Carbohydrates are particularly important as a source of energy for (choose one):
   a. low-intensity activities
   b. low- to medium-intensity activities
   c. medium-intensity activities
   d. medium- to high-intensity activities
5. Why is it important to include minerals in a balanced diet?

Read about it

Gain further advice about portion sizes by reading the following article:
www.tinyurl.com/y7kkwdl6

1.1.3 Rest and recovery

Rest is vital for any person. However, it becomes even more important after periods of exercise. Rest allows for **recovery**. Rest is considered to be a time when a performer undertakes little or no exertion. Recovery on the other hand is what a performer does to allow repair of the body. Thus, rest can be an intended action to allow recovery.

Sleep

Sleep is a vital component of a person's rest. You can remember some of the main variables affected by good or bad sleep using the acronym HEAL. This stands for:

- **H**ealth: mental health is affected by sleep. People who worry a lot tend not to sleep as well. Equally, physical health is affected by sleep, as a good sleep helps the body to recover and repair, ready for the day and exercise ahead. Micro-tears in muscles can repair and lactic acid is gradually broken down.
- **A**ttitude: people with a positive attitude towards sleep tend to sleep better. Most people aim for 7–9 hours per night and often try to relax in advance of going to bed.
- **E**nvironment: temperature, noise levels and light all play a part in a person's ability to sleep. Most people sleep better when it's dark, not too noisy and not too bright.
- **L**ifestyle: what you eat and drink can affect your sleep. Alcohol and caffeinated drinks do not help sleep patterns.

Recovery between physical activity sessions

Some performers take further steps in trying to recover from physical exertion. A cool down helps the initial stages of recovery. However, further examples include **dietary manipulation**, **massage** and ice baths.

Diet can be manipulated to improve performance or to assist in the recovery process. This includes the intake of fluid to rehydrate. Performers may also need to replenish food stores – for example, carbohydrate stores which have been used during exercise and protein to assist in growth and repair of muscles.

Massage involves rubbing and 'kneading' of the muscles. It helps to reduce pain and encourages blood flow through the muscles. This helps to flush out waste products.

Ice baths can also be used, where the performer stays in the ice bath for a few minutes. During this time many of the body's blood vessels to the muscles/extremities reduce in diameter forcing blood to the body's core (for example, vital organs). When the performer leaves the ice bath the vessels increase in diameter allowing oxygen-rich blood to flush the muscles. This helps to remove waste products and prevent DOMS – the delayed onset of muscle soreness.

Rest between physical activity repetitions

The amount of rest required between physical activity repetitions will vary depending on the type and intensity of the exercise and the intent behind what is being performed. The correct balance of work to rest allows the correct energy system in the body to be stressed, while allowing the body's systems to recover suitably in-between the work periods. A 'full' rest between repetitions would only be used if the person does not want to overload and cause adaptation, or because the repetition is so hard that the stress placed on the body requires full rest before trying the repetition again. However, rest periods may deliberately be cut short to ensure the next repetition is under more stress and overload – thus causing a greater adaptation of the body. Here are two examples:

1 A performer sprints for 100 metres.

   The body naturally takes approximately 2–3 minutes to recover fully from such a sprint.

   A performer takes the full 2–3 minutes to ensure they are fully recovered for the next sprint. They may be purely concentrating on technique.

2 A performer sprints for 100 metres.

   The body naturally takes approximately 2–3 minutes to recover fully from such a sprint.

   The performer takes only 45 seconds rest, so that the next sprint is harder than the first, leading to adaptation of the body.

Other factors which determine the amount of rest between repetitions include:

- fitness level – trained individuals recover more quickly
- age – elderly people take longer to recover.

When weight training, the work:rest ratio is crucial in achieving the main objective. You aim to put an appropriate amount of stress on the muscle/s, using the correct energy system, while allowing the muscle/s to recover appropriately in between sets. If a performer is lifting very heavy weights, the stress on the muscles is huge. Thus, it would be recommended that a suitable period of rest is placed between each set so that the muscles are ready to carry out another repetition. A common heavy weights training programme for strength would see 85 per cent or more of your **1 rep max** (one repetition maximum) being lifted, two to six reps, two to six sets, and two to five minutes of rest in between each set.

Key word

1 rep max: the maximum weight that can be lifted in one repetition.

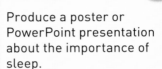

Activity

List the ways that you aim to recover after exercise. Do you do more than simply rest?

Activity

Produce a poster or PowerPoint presentation about the importance of sleep.

Read about it

Read about rest and recovery here: www.tinyurl.com/ycpb3ao2

Read about rest between repetitions in the gym here: www.tinyurl.com/ya9lllv6

Read about the importance of sleep here:

www.tinyurl.com/yaphwak5

www.tinyurl.com/ycj2qmsa

Figure 2.5 Rest is an important part of recovery.

Test yourself

1   What is the difference between rest and recovery?
2   How much sleep should an average adult have per night?
3   Describe one way to recover other than simply resting.

1.1.4 Other factors

Many factors affect the health and fitness of a person. Training and nutrition from a balanced diet can assist performers, but other factors can result in negative effects. These factors include drugs, smoking, alcohol and stress. The negative effects of each of these is shown in Table 2.2.

Table 2.2 The negative effects of drugs, smoking, alcohol and stress

Factor	Negative effect
Recreational drugs: drugs which are taken for recreational rather than performance-enhancing capabilities.	Recreational drugs include the likes of cannabis, cocaine, and ecstasy. Cannabis has been linked to mental health problems and can be a factor in the development of asthma. Cocaine can cause damage to the cartilage of the nose and can increase blood pressure. Ecstasy has links to depression, anxiety and problems associated with regulating body temperature.
Performing-enhancing drugs (PEDs): taken purely to enhance performance.	Performance-enhancing drugs are illegally taken by some athletes. Drugs like diuretics can help athletes to lose weight (e.g. boxers) but can lead to dehydration, low blood pressure and muscle cramps. Anabolic steroids (illegally taken to increase muscle mass) can lead to high blood pressure, damage to the liver, kidneys and heart. They can also cause hormonal imbalance, such as testicles shrinking or women developing more body hair.
Smoking	Smoking can irritate the respiratory system. It reduces the lungs' ability to function efficiently and causes breathlessness. Gaseous exchange at the alveoli in the lungs is negatively affected as mucus builds up on the lung passages – causing a person to cough.
Alcohol	Alcohol is relatively harmless in small quantities, but in larger quantities it can cause behavioural changes, addiction and liver damage.
Stress	Some stress can be good for you. This is called 'eustress' – e.g. being stressed enough to get out of bed or to go to work. However, most stress is bad for a person's health. It can increase blood pressure, put stress on the heart, weaken your immune system and affect hormone balance (see Figure 2.6).

Key words

Recreational drugs: drugs taken for recreational purposes rather than performance-enhancing capabilities.

Performance-enhancing drugs: illegally taken drugs, taken in order to enhance performance rather than for recreational reasons.

Read about it

Read about the effects of smoking, alcohol, drugs and stress using the links below.

Smoking: **www.tinyurl.com/yaf4ohqf**

Alcohol: **www.tinyurl.com/ln242ah**

Drugs: **www.tinyurl.com/ybam22go**

Stress: **www.tinyurl.com/ybrgc9em**

Activity

Design a poster to warn students at your school or college of the dangers of a recreational drug.

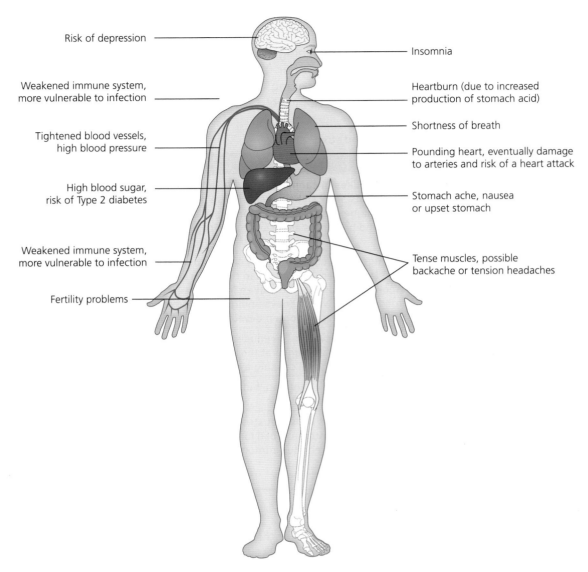

Risk of depression

Weakened immune system, more vulnerable to infection

Tightened blood vessels, high blood pressure

High blood sugar, risk of Type 2 diabetes

Weakened immune system, more vulnerable to infection

Fertility problems

Insomnia

Heartburn (due to increased production of stomach acid)

Shortness of breath

Pounding heart, eventually damage to arteries and risk of a heart attack

Stomach ache, nausea or upset stomach

Tense muscles, possible backache or tension headaches

Figure 2.6 The negative effects of stress on the body

Activity

Design a poster to display at a local gymnasium to warn attendees of the dangers of taking anabolic steroids.

Activity

Test a partner on the negative effects of different factors. Give them the terms: smoking, alcohol, recreational drugs, PEDs or stress and encourage them to tell you negative side effects.

Test yourself

1 State two negative effects of smoking on the body.
2 What is the difference between a recreational drug and a performance-enhancing drug (PED)?
3 Why should we be encouraged to keep our stress levels low?

Remember

● Lifestyle is a choice which is affected by factors such as disposable income, facilities available and time.

● The National Health Service has guidelines for the amount of physical activity that you should do. These guidelines are divided up into four different age categories.

● A balanced diet contains a suitable amount of all the nutrients the body requires.

● An energy balance is achieved when the amount consumed equals the amount needed for energy that day.

● Carbohydrates are the body's favoured energy source.

● Recovery methods are intended to help the body to recover and repair. Rest is likely to form part of the recovery process.

● PEDs and recreational drugs (including smoking tobacco and drinking alcohol) result in negative side effects that affect a person's performance.

Review questions

1 What is meant by the term 'active lifestyle'?
2 State three factors that affect a person's lifestyle choices.
3 Explain how an appropriate amount of sleep affects physical and mental health.
4 What percentage of carbohydrates, fat and protein is suggested in a balanced diet?
5 What is meant by the term 'sedentary lifestyle'.
6 Explain the relationship between rest and repetitions.
7 Describe the relationship between rest and recovery.
8 Give one reason why an athlete may decide to take a diuretic as an illegal PED. Also state one side effect.
9 What is the difference between a recreational drug and a performance-enhancing drug?
10 State three negative consequences of suffering from stress.

Learning outcome 2: understand how to test and develop components of fitness

For the second learning outcome you will learn:

- how to prepare, carry out and collect data on the appropriate fitness test for each component of health-related fitness
- how to prepare, carry out and collect data on the appropriate fitness test for each component of skill-related fitness.
- about the use of normative data and re-testing
- different training methods and how to apply them to support individual goals
- how to calculate maximal heart rate and what percentage to work at when aiming for aerobic or anaerobic improvement
- how to calculate 1 rep max and how to use this to work with a suitable number of sets and reps.

2.1 Fitness testing

2.1.1 Health-related fitness

Table 2.3 gives the name and explanation of how to carry out health-related fitness tests and how to collect data. All of these tests are **maximal** – requiring 100 per cent effort.

Table 2.3 Health-related fitness tests

Component and test	How to prepare for, carry out and collect data
Cardiovascular endurance (multi-stage fitness test)	<ul><li>Prepare a coned area – cones 20 m apart.</li><li>Participant runs 20 m in time with bleeps.</li><li>Time between bleeps gets shorter as the level increases.</li><li>Participant keeps running until they cannot keep up with the bleeps.</li><li>Score is recorded as a level and bleep. For example, 3/3 (see Table 2.4) corresponds to level 3, bleep 3.</li><li>Compare with **national averages** (Table 2.4) and use to predict a VO2 max score (the maximum amount of oxygen that can be consumed per minute).</li></ul>
Muscular strength (handgrip **dynamometer**)	<ul><li>Have a handgrip dynamometer ready at zero.</li><li>Dynamometer should be held in the participant's dominant hand.</li><li>Squeeze with maximum effort and record score on dial.</li><li>Repeat ×3 and record best score.</li><li>Compare with national averages (Table 2.5).</li></ul>

Muscular endurance (sit-up test)	● Have abdominal conditioning test CD ready to play. ● Lie down in the sit-up position, while a partner supports the ankles. ● Sit-up on the bleep and down on the bleep. ● A progressive test – the bleeps get faster. ● Score = how many sit-ups you complete. ● Compare to national averages (see Table 2.6).
Body composition (skinfold **caliper** test)	● Have skinfold calipers ready. ● Record by pinching the skinfold amount at seven sites on the body – triceps, biceps, subscapular, supraspinale, abdominal, thigh, calf area. ● Record scores in millimetres at the seven main skinfold sites (see above). ● Compare with national averages (see Table 2.7).
Flexibility (sit and reach test)	● Have sit and reach box ready. ● Start in sitting position on the floor with legs straight. ● No shoes to be worn and feet should be flat against the sit and reach board. ● Slider (if available) should be set to 14 cm to be in line with the toes. ● Reach forward and push the slider as far as possible. ● Record score in cm. ● Compare with national averages (see Table 2.8).

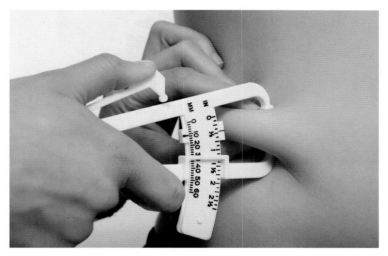

Figure 2.7 Skinfold calipers to measure body fat and determine body composition

Key words

Maximal: working with 100 per cent effort.

National average: a table of normative data that provides categorised scores for test results.

Dynamometer: device used to measure strength in the hand.

Caliper: device used to measure skinfold to calculate body composition.

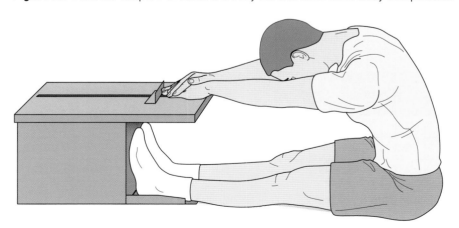

Figure 2.8 Sit and reach test

Figure 2.9 Completing the sit-up test

Table 2.4 Cardiovascular endurance (aerobic power) test – multi-stage fitness test ratings

Males							
	Very poor	Poor	Fair	Average	Good	Very good	Excellent
12–13 yrs	< 3/3	3/4–5/1	5/2–6/4	6/5–7/5	7/6–8/8	8/9–10/9	> 10/9
14–15 yrs	< 4/7	4/7–6/1	6/2–7/4	7/5–8/9	8/10–9/8	9/9–12/2	> 12/2
16–17 yrs	< 5/1	5/1–6/8	6/9–8/2	8/3–9/9	9/10–11/3	11/4–13/7	> 13/7
Females							
	Very poor	Poor	Fair	Average	Good	Very good	Excellent
12–13 yrs	< 2/6	2/6–3/5	3/6–5/1	5/2–6/1	6/2–7/4	7/5–9/3	> 9/3
14–15 yrs	< 3/3	3/4–5/2	5/3–6/4	6/5–7/5	7/6–8/7	8/8–10/7	> 10/7
16–17 yrs	< 4/2	4/2–5/6	5/7–7/1	7/2–8/4	8/5–9/7	9/8–11/10	> 11/11

Source: Adapted from Beep Test Ratings www.topendsports.com

Table 2.5 Muscular strength (handgrip dynamometer) strength test ratings (in kg)

Males			
	Weak	**Normal**	**Strong**
10–11 yrs	< 12.6	12.6–22.4	> 22.4
12–13 yrs	< 19.4	19.4–31.2	> 31.2
14–15 yrs	< 28.5	28.5–44.3	> 44.3
16–17 yrs	< 32.6	32.6–52.4	> 52.4
18–19 yrs	< 35.7	35.7–55.5	> 55.5

Females			
	Weak	**Normal**	**Strong**
10–11 yrs	< 11.8	11.8–21.6	> 21.6
12–13 yrs	< 14.6	14.6–24.4	> 24.4
14–15 yrs	< 15.5	15.5–27.3	> 27.3
16–17 yrs	< 17.2	17.2–29.0	> 29.0
18–19 yrs	< 19.2	19.2–31.0	> 31.0

Source: Camry Electronic Hand Dynamometer Instruction manual, www.topendsports.com

Table 2.6 Abdominal conditioning test ratings

Stage	Total sit-ups	Males	Females
1	20	Poor	Poor
2	42	Poor	Fair
3	64	Fair	Fair
4	89	Fair	Good
5	116	Good	Good
6	146	Good	Very Good
7	180	Excellent	Excellent
8	217	Excellent	Excellent

Source: Adapted from NCF Abdominal Curl Conditioning Test www.topendsports.com

Table 2.7 Skinfold measurement test ratings (in mm)

		Excellent	**Good**	**Average**	**Below average**	**Poor**
Normal	**Male**	60–80	81–90	91–110	111–150	150+
	Female	70–90	91–100	101–120	121–150	150+
Athletic	**Male**	40–60	61–80	81–100	101–130	130+
	Female	50–70	71–85	86–110	111–130	130+

Source: Data supplied by Top End Sports www.topendsports.com

Activity

Watch the multi-stage fitness test being completed: **www.tinyurl.com/ybch6u65**

Watch the skinfold caliper test being completed: **www.tinyurl.com/y8agck8d**

Table 2.8 Sit and reach test ratings

	Men		Women	
	cm	inches	cm	inches
Super	> +27	> +10.5	> +30	> +11.5
Excellent	+17 to +27	+6.5 to +10.5	+21 to +30	+8.0 to +11.5
Good	+6 to +16	+2.5 to +6.0	+11 to +20	+4.5 to +7.5
Average	0 to +5	0 to +2.0	+1 to +10	+0.5 to +4.0
Fair	−8 to −1	−3.0 to −0.5	−7 to 0	−2.5 to 0
Poor	−20 to −9	−7.5 to −3.5	−15 to −8	−6.0 to −3.0
Very poor	< −20	< −7.5	< −15	< −6.0

Source: Data supplied by Top End Sports www.topendsports.com

20 metres

Figure 2.10 The multi-stage fitness test is run over 20 m shuttles.

Read about it

Read about the body composition test: **www.tinyurl.com/3ez8k2a**
Read about the multi-stage fitness test: **www.tinyurl.com/y7sy6qlu**

Test yourself

1 Name a suitable test to measure cardiovascular endurance.
2 State how to do the handheld handgrip dynamometer test.
3 What distance is a shuttle in the multi-stage fitness test?
4 State how to do the sit and reach test.
5 What does the abdominal conditioning sit-up test measure?

2.1.2 Skill-related fitness

Table 2.9 gives the name and explanation of how to carry out skill-related fitness tests and how to collect data. All of these tests are maximal – requiring 100 per cent effort.

Table 2.9 Skill-related fitness tests

Component and test	How to prepare for, carry out and collect data
Agility (Illinois agility test)	• Set out the cones. • Performer starts face down on the floor. • The test involves running around the cones (10 m × 5 m) as fast as possible (it is a maximal test). • It is timed in seconds. • Compare with national averages (see Table 2.10).
Speed	• Measure a 30 m running area. • There should be a flying start (on the move). • Sprint 30 m as fast as possible. • It is timed in seconds. • Record time and compare with national averages (see Table 2.11).
Co-ordination (wall toss test)	• Start with a ball (e.g. tennis ball) in one hand. • Stand 2 m from the wall (both feet need to be together). • When 'go' is called the time starts – test is 30 seconds long. • Throw the ball against the wall so as to catch the ball with the opposite hand. • Count the number of catches. • Repeat as many times as possible within the 30 seconds. • Two attempts are allowed and then compare with national averages (see Table 2.12).
Power (vertical jump test)	• Ensure the wall ruler is set to bottom point. • Stand with the feet flat and push a wall ruler with fingertips (as high as possible) – this provides the participant's 'zero point'. • From a standing position, participant jump as high as possible, and mark the ruler with chalk. • Record the jump height (in cm). • Compare score with national averages (see Table 2.13).
Balance (standing stork test)	• Have the stopwatch ready. • Start balanced on two flat feet. • Place hands on the hips. • Lift one leg so that the toes of the lifted leg touch the inside of the knee. • Raise the heel on the planted leg (this is when the stopwatch should start) • Balance for as long as possible – until balance is lost or toes at the inside of the knee are moved. • Record time in minutes/seconds. • Compare score with national averages (see Table 2.14).
Reaction time (ruler drop test)	• Ensure a one-metre ruler is available. • One person holds the metre ruler at zero. • Participant places their thumb and index finger of their dominant hand at 50 cm (not touching the ruler). • With no warning, the ruler is dropped. • The participant reacts to the drop by catching the ruler as soon as possible. • Record the score (distance from 50 cm that participant caught ruler). • Three attempts are allowed and then compare scores with national averages (see Table 2.15).

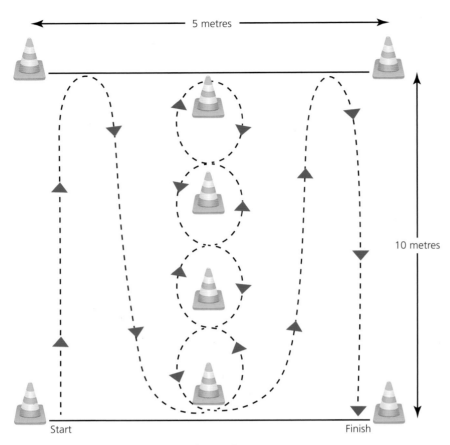

Figure 2.11 Illinois agility test running path

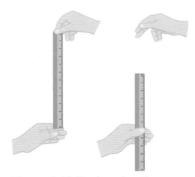

Figure 2.12 Performing the ruler drop test

Table 2.10 Illiniois agility test ratings

Rating	Males	Females
Excellent	< 15.2	< 17.0
Above average	16.1–15.2	17.9–17.0
Average	18.1–16.2	21.7–18.0
Below average	18.3–18.2	23.0–21.8
Poor	> 18.3	> 23.0

Source: Davis, B. *et al.* (2000) *Physical Education and the Study of Sport*

Table 2.11 Speed (30 m sprint) test ratings (in seconds)

	Male	Female
Excellent	< 4.0	< 4.5
Above average	4.2–4.0	4.6–4.5
Average	4.4–4.3	4.8–4.7
Below average	4.6–4.5	5.0–4.9
Poor	> 4.6	> 5.0

Source: Brian Mac Sports Coach, adapted from B. Davis et al (2000) *Physical Education and the Study of Sport*

Table 2.13 Vertical jump test ratings

	Males		Females	
Rating	(inches)	(cm)	(inches)	(cm)
Excellent	> 28	> 70	> 24	> 60
Very good	24–28	61–70	20–24	51–60
Above average	20–24	51–60	16–20	41–50
Average	16–20	41–50	12–16	31–40
Below average	12–16	31–40	8–12	21–30
Poor	8–12	21–30	4–8	11–20
Very poor	< 8	< 21	< 4	< 11

Source: www.topendsports.com/testing/tests/home-vertical-jump.htm

Table 2.12 Co-ordination (wall toss test) test ratings

Rating	Score (in 30 seconds)
Excellent	> 35
Good	30–35
Average	20–29
Fair	15–19
Poor	< 15

Source: adapted from Alternate Hand Wall Toss Test www.topendsports.com

Table 2.14 Stork balance test ratings (in seconds)

Rating	Males	Females
Excellent	< 50	< 30
Above average	41–50	23–30
Average	31–40	16–22
Below average	20–30	10–15
Poor	> 20	> 10

Source: Johnson and Nelson (1979) *Practical Measurements for Evaluation in Physical Education*

Table 2.15 Reaction time (ruler drop test) test ratings

Excellent	Above average	Average	Below average	Poor
< 7.5 cm	7.5–9 cm	15.9–20.4 cm	20.4–28 cm	> 28 cm

Source: norms, adapted from Davis (2000), for 16- to 19-year-olds

Read about it

Read about the ruler drop reaction time test: **www.tinyurl.com/y8dloakn**

Read about the co-ordination (wall toss) test: **www.tinyurl.com/y7kezfrz**

Test yourself

1 How do you carry out the wall toss test?

2 How do you collect data for the Illinois agility test?

3 How is the score collected for the vertical jump test?

4 Name a suitable test for balance.

2.1.3 Using data

As part of this course, it is important that you know how to collect, use and analyse data to evaluate levels of fitness. Sections 2.1.1 and 2.1.2 show you how to collect the fitness test data. However, once it is collected it should be analysed. Analysis generally involves using national averages, which are displayed in tables as normative data.

Normative data

Normative data is data that is gathered from a large range of people to form categories of what is normally scored. For example, normative data can be national standards, which you can compare yourself with. If we use the example of the multi-stage fitness test, the normative data table is Table 2.4 on page 92.

Normative data is important as it puts a person's fitness test score into perspective – how well have I done compared with what is normally scored?

If you were to try a fairly quick and easy test like the wall toss test (to test co-ordination), Table 2.12 would be used as normative scores.

It is also important to understand the importance of the words **validity** and **reliability**:

- Validity – a fitness test is only valid if the score is calculated using the correct procedures.
- Reliability – a fitness test is only valid if when repeated, similar results are gained. You can remember the term **RE RE RE** (**re**liable tests, can be **re**peated and give similar **re**sults).

Key words

Normative data: refers to the use of national standards to show what is normal, excellent, good, average, below average or poor.

Validity: a fitness test is only valid if the score is calculated using the correct procedures.

Reliability: a fitness test is only valid if when repeated, similar results are gained.

Test and re-test

Having taken a test it is normal that training is devised to improve fitness. Tests are not used to improve fitness, they are used to **measure** fitness. Thus, once training has taken place, the most obvious way to check improvement is by re-testing. Re-testing will determine whether training has been successful and how much improvement has taken place.

Figure 2.13 Test for leg power

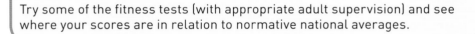

Figure 2.14 Train for leg power

Figure 2.15 Re-test for leg power

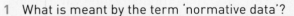

Activity

Try some of the fitness tests (with appropriate adult supervision) and see where your scores are in relation to normative national averages.

Test yourself

1 What is meant by the term 'normative data'?
2 What normative data exists for fitness tests?
3 Why should you test and re-test fitness?
4 Do fitness tests improve fitness levels?

2.2, 2.3 Training methods; optimising a health and fitness programme

2.2.1, 2.3.1, 2.3.2 Training methods, heart-rate training zones, repetitions and sets

This section of the book will combine the varying training methods that can be used (2.2.1) with how to optimise a fitness programme (2.3). This incorporates appropriate heart-rate training zones (2.3.1) and repetitions and sets (2.3.2).

Once fitness tests have been carried out, performers tend to plan a fitness training programme to improve their fitness levels before re-testing. Different training methods can be used, each with their own unique advantages and disadvantages in terms of achieving individual training goals.

The main training methods you need to know are:

- interval training
- circuit training
- fartlek training
- continuous training
- resistance and body weight training
- cross training (combining two or more methods).

Interval training

Interval training is any type of training that involves altering periods of **work** with periods of rest. It usually involves periods of intense exercise (working hard) with periods of rest or low-intensity exercise. However, the work periods can be altered in length and intensity to mimic the sport being trained for. The training goal can be met by changing what the work:rest ratio is.

As interval raining can be altered to suit the needs of a performer, the energy system being stressed can vary. High-intensity interval training (HIIT) involves short, high-intensity periods of work, which improves the anaerobic system, although some research suggests it also improves the aerobic system. The **anaerobic training zone** tends to be anything over 80 per cent of maximal heart rate.

Key words

Interval training: any type of training that involves altering periods of work with periods of rest.

Work: a level of exertion which is harder than normal.

Anaerobic training zone: anything over 80 per cent of maximal heart rate.

You can also vary the length of the work:rest intervals in order to gain different benefits – see Tables 2.16 and 2.17.

Table 2.16 Interval training to improve 400 m performance

Aim: to improve 400 m performance
Training needs: anaerobic, as 400m is an anaerobic event
Interval training design: high-intensity burst of work for up to 60 seconds with 30 seconds rest in-between
(NB: during high-intensity periods, the performer should be working at 80% of their heart rate maximum or higher.)

Table 2.17 Interval training to improve general fitness

Aim: to improve general fitness as new to training
Training need: to improve aerobic and anaerobic energy systems
Interval training design: high-intensity work for 30 seconds with 3 minutes of low-intensity work in-between. The low-intensity work can be shortened as fitness improves.
(NB: during high intensity periods, the performer should be working at 80% of their heart rate maximum or higher.)

Activity

Try to think of three sporting activities that would better suit the changing intensity of interval training compared with continuous training (working at the same intensity).

Fartlek training (see page 104) and weight training can also be deemed as interval training due to the changing intensity (for example, the rest between lifting a set of weights). Fartlek can be altered to stress the aerobic and anaerobic energy systems.

Table 2.18 Advantages and disadvantages of interval training

Advantages	Disadvantages
● burns calories quickly	● injury more possible at a high intensity
● can be completed fairly quickly	● participants must be motivated to achieve the correct intensity
● work:rest ratio can be designed to meet the training goal	

Test yourself

1 What is a work:rest ratio?

2 What would a suitable work:rest ratio be for specific anaerobic training goals?

3 What does HIIT stand for?

Read about it

Find out about examples of interval training here: **www.tinyurl.com/ybspw9we**

Circuit training

Circuit training involves exercises being organised in different areas or **stations**. Each station can be completely different from the next. Completion of all of the stations is called a 'circuit'. The amount of rest between each station or after each circuit can be changed as necessary.

It is common that a circuit is designed to train different components of fitness and work on different muscles/body parts. Examples of common circuit training exercises include: shuttle runs, step-ups, sit-ups, press-ups, seated dips, squats, straddle jumps, squat jumps, burpees, etc. Circuits can be designed to suit a specific training goal (for example, if strength is desired, the stations can involve strength exercises).

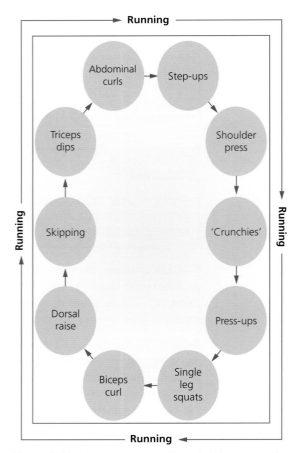

Figure 2.16 An example circuit containing several stations

Energy demand and intensity

The intensity of the work periods at stations can be changed. High-intensity work rate (over 80 per cent of maximal heart rate) will use the anaerobic system, whereas low-intensity work can use the aerobic system (60–80 per cent of maximal heart rate). Performers should make sure the stations involve muscles/movements and energy demands which are suitable for their particular sport or performance goal.

Figure 2.17 Kettle bells are sometimes used within a circuit training programme.

Read about it

Read the section on HIIT circuit training at: **www.tinyurl.com/5a77um**

Table 2.19 Advantages and disadvantages of circuit training

Advantages	Disadvantages
<ul><li>can be designed for fitness needs for any hport or training programme</li><li>easy to vary what is at each station</li><li>exercises can be simple (e.g. press-ups, sit-ups, etc.)</li><li>progression and overload are easy to apply (i.e. increase the amount of work and reduce the rest)</li></ul>	<ul><li>may require a large area of space</li><li>may require specialist equipment (e.g. kettle bells)</li><li>can be difficult to work out the correct work:rest ratio</li></ul>

Test yourself

1 What is a station as used in circuit training?
2 Give three examples of commonly used exercises in a circuit.
3 At what intensity of maximal heart rate would a performer train at to make aerobic gains?

Fartlek training

Fartlek training is a Swedish name for 'speed play' whereby the work-rate intensity and **terrain** change from high to lower and back to higher. This is the key difference to standard interval training as the intensity **and** terrain change (for example, walk, jog, sprint, jog (hill), walk, etc.).

Fartlek is commonly used by team games players (such as football, hockey, netball and rugby). This is because such sports require the intensity to change at different points in the game. The main aim of fartlek training is to improve aerobic endurance, but higher-intensity sections will also improve the anaerobic energy system. The amount of walking, jogging, sprinting, etc. can be altered to stress the aerobic and anaerobic energy systems. For someone who is developing a base level of fitness, fartlek is good as it can improve both aerobic and anaerobic energy systems.

Key words

Fartlek: fartlek training is a Swedish name for 'speed play' whereby the work rate intensity and terrain change from high to lower and back to higher.

Terrain: the surface or conditions upon which one is running.

Read about it

Read about fartlek training here: www.tinyurl.com/y8hb88t6

Activity

Watch the clip about fartlek training: www.tinyurl.com/7oztqmc

Figure 2.18 Fartlek training involves changing intensity and terrain. This may involve the use of hill running.

Table 2.20 Advantages and disadvantages of fartlek training

Advantages	Disadvantages
• results in improved cardiovascular fitness and anaerobic fitness • mixes continuous training with interval training • can be done anywhere with little to no equipment – often done around the surrounding environment (e.g. streets and hills)	• hard to know when to change intensity • can result in muscle soreness as a result of hill running

Continuous training

Continuous training involves any exercise that can be maintained without rest and repeated over and over (such as running, cycling and swimming). It is used to improve cardiovascular endurance and involves working at a constant rate or intensity. This is often referred to as **steady-state exercise**. Any sport that requires the need to 'keep going' for a long period of time can benefit from continuous training – for example, marathon running, football (90 minutes), rugby (80 minutes), etc. However, athletes performing long-distance running where the intensity remains relatively stable can benefit the most. Continuous training is good for those starting out on a fitness programme as it improves their aerobic fitness, allowing them to slowly build up the intensity they can work at.

Energy system and intensity

Continuous training is intended to work the aerobic energy system. To do this, it is most common to use your heart rate as a guide. This is known as working at your **aerobic training zone**. Maintaining aerobic activity will reduce fat content, and suitably stress the heart so that it gets stronger and potentially larger and more efficient. Performers may be able to work steadily for longer in their games or events. Continuous training usually involves working without rests, for approximately 20 minutes or more.

Calculating the aerobic training zone

Calculating the aerobic training zone for continuous training involves using your heart rate as a guide. This involves calculating your maximum heart rate in beats per minute and working at a percentage of this:

- calculate maximum heart rate (220 – age)
- calculate aerobic training zone (60 – 80 per cent of maximal heart rate).

Although continuous training is appropriate to team games, try to remember that the varying intensity of interval/fartlek training may be more beneficial as it matches the changing intensity required to play team sports.

Figure 2.19 Steady-state running is a common way to carry out continuous training.

Table 2.21 Advantages and disadvantages of continuous training

Advantages	Disadvantages
● can be done with little or no equipment – just run or swim, etc. ● simple and easy to do ● can be done anywhere (e.g. inside, outside, etc.) ● good way to improve aerobic fitness/cardiovascular endurance	● can be boring repeating the same thing over and over ● repetitive strain injuries can occur ● can take a large amount of time (e.g. to run or cycle a long distance) ● very few activities are completed at a constant intensity, therefore it matches very few sports

Activity

Go for a jog wearing a heart-rate monitor and see if you can stay in your aerobic training zone (60–80% of 220 – age).

Read about it

Read about the advantages and disadvantages of continuous training:
www.tinyurl.com/y8d59zzg

Test yourself

1 How is maximal heart rate calculated?
2 How is the aerobic training zone calculated?
3 What energy system is particularly stressed by using continuous running?
4 Name an athletic event for which a performer's performance may improve if they used continuous training.

Resistance and body weight training

All forms of resistance training involve the performer using something that resists against their muscles. This can be something like a weight, a resistance machine or even using the gravitational pull of your own body.

Weight training

Weight training involves using some resistance to develop muscular strength or muscular endurance. The weight being lifted may well be a free weight (dumbbell or **kettle bell**) or a resistance machine. The lifting of weights tends to involve **sets** and **reps** whereby:

- a repetition (rep) is one complete lift of the weight
- a set is a group of several repetitions.

In all types of weight training, it is vital that the correct technique is adopted. Particular care should be taken with the performer's back – they should maintain a straight back as much as possible. Weight training may also involve a 'spotter' to spot for any difficulty when lifting a heavy weight.

Key words

Kettle bell: a type of free weight.

Set: a collection of repetitions that occur before a period of rest.

Rep: a single completion of one lift of the resistance being used.

Read about it

Read about many of the body weight exercises you could do without the need for weights or equipment: **www.tinyurl.com/ y8o4ow3w**.

Figure 2.20 Using free weights

Figure 2.21 Using kettle bells

Energy demand and intensity

The intensity of the weight being lifted should be chosen to meet the intended outcome. Thus, heavy weights tend to be for muscular strength whereas lighter weights tend to be for muscular endurance. To calculate the intensity, the concept of a 1 rep max is used. This is the maximum weight that can safely be lifted in one repetition. As a basic rule the following guidelines can be used:

- power – 2–4 reps for 2–4 sets
- strength – 5–8 reps for 2–6 sets
- muscular endurance – 12–20 reps for 2–6 sets.

Improvements in strength as a result of weight training can aid sports performance (for example, the strength used in a rugby tackle could improve). Equally, improvements in muscular endurance may help an athlete (for example, to maintain a race pace in a 1500 m event). Weight training can improve body shape and body image – potentially improving self-esteem.

Body weight exercises are a simple and effective way to gain strength using your own body weight. **Gravity** wants to pull your body down but you can either control the speed at which your body falls or resist against gravity by making the body rise up from the ground. Body weight exercises like press-ups, sit-ups, plank and squats help to improve balance, flexibility, and strength without the need for machinery or extra equipment.

Key words

Gravity: the natural pull towards the earth's core.

Figure 2.22 Press-ups can be used as a way to increase strength using one's own body weight.

Table 2.22 Advantages and disadvantages of resistance training

Advantages	Disadvantages
● intensity can easily be changed ● relevant to virtually every sport or fitness aim ● improves strength/muscular endurance	● heavy weights can be damaging to children ● incorrect technique can result in injury ● heavy weights require a 'spotter'

Activity

Using a partner, try to design a weight-training session to improve their strength. Include eight different exercises and calculate their 1 rep max, sets and reps for them.

Test yourself

1 What is meant by 1 rep max?
2 What is a suitable number of sets and reps to improve muscular endurance?
3 What is a suitable number of sets and reps to improve power?

Cross training

Cross training is a term used for any exercise programme that makes use of two or more differing training types. For example, for a runner this might be their decision to mix continuous running with weight training. In this example, their cardiovascular endurance could be improved through the running and their muscular endurance through the use of weight training.

A person leading a sedentary lifestyle may decide to follow the cross training programme shown in Figure 2.23.

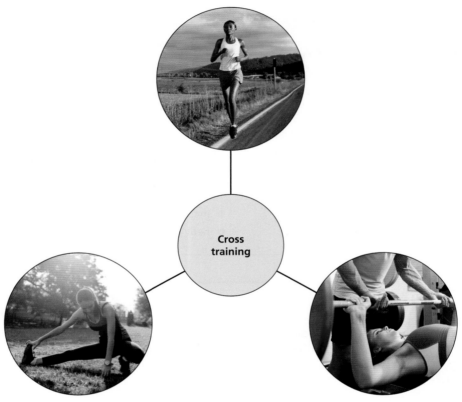

Figure 2.23 Possible components of a cross training programme

Table 2.23 Advantages of cross training

There are some major advantages to undertaking a cross training programme
Reduced risk of injury: By spreading the stress over different muscles and joints, while using differing movements, the body is not experiencing particular stress on one specific body part.
Weight loss: One significant advantage of cross training is that it is conducive to losing weight.
Variety: Most people give up training or exercise due to boredom. By using a cross training programme there is variety and different training types to look forward to.
Specific gains: A person who plays a sport that requires lots of different components of fitness can target these components within different training methods.

Test yourself

1 What is cross training?

2 Suggest three types of training a person starting out on a basic fitness programme may decide to use and why.

3 State three different advantages of using a cross training programme.

Remember

- The correct protocol to carry out a test must be followed in order to ensure its validity.

- Normative data is available in the form of national averages. This takes a large sample of the population and shows what is categorised as poor, below average, average, good and excellent scores.

- Maximal effort in a test requires a participant to give 100 per cent effort.

- Re-testing of fitness tests allows a performer to see if improvement has taken place as a result of training.

- Continuous training is used to improve aerobic performance.

- Interval training involves a work:rest ratio that can be altered to suit the desired outcome.

- Body weight can be used as resistance to improve strength without the need for free weights or resistance machines.

- Fartlek training involves changing the intensity and terrain.

- Maximal heart rate is calculated as 220 – age. For aerobic gains an aerobic zone should be used working at 60–80 per cent of maximal heart rate.

- Cross training involves using two or more training methods.

Review questions

1 With reference to fitness testing, what is 'normative data'?

2 Describe the protocol for the ruler drop reaction-time test.

3 Describe the protocol for the multi-stage fitness test.

4 What is meant by the term 'reliable' when referring to fitness tests?

5 Which type of training is most likely to be used regularly by a marathon runner?

6 Give two disadvantages of resistance training.

7 With reference to weight training, state how the sets to reps differs when training power, strength or muscular endurance.

8 State a suitable training zone for improving cardiovascular endurance.

9 Describe how cross training may reduce the chances of developing an injury.

Learning outcome 3: understand how to apply health and fitness analyses and set goals

In this learning outcome, you will develop understanding of:

- health and fitness analysis tools including
  - PAR-Q
  - lifestyle questionnaire
  - food diary
  - client progress review
- how to apply the acronym SMART when setting health and fitness goals based on data.

3.1 Health and fitness analysis and goal setting

3.1.1 Health and fitness analysis tools

Health and fitness analysis tools can be used in order to collect, use and evaluate a person's suitability for specific types of training or exercise. They can also form part of a general overview of lifestyle and progress. The main methods to be aware of are:

- **PAR-Q** (physical-activity readiness questionnaire)
- lifestyle **questionnaire**
- **food diary**
- client progress review.

For each of these analysis tools, you should know how to collect, use, analyse and evaluate data in order to suggest improvements.

PAR-Q (physical-activity readiness questionnaire)

PAR- Q is a sensible step for an individual to take in determining whether to increase the amount of physical activity in their life. It is collected via a simple 'yes/no' questionnaire and aims to identify the small number of people for whom physical activity might be unsuitable on the grounds of medical advice. It is a self-screening tool that an individual can use on their own. However, the questionnaire can also be analysed by a coach for any obvious medical information that can be evaluated as to whether physical activity may be inadvisable for their client.

Key words

PAR-Q: a simple 'yes/no' questionnaire that aims to identify the small number of people for whom physical activity might be unsuitable on the grounds of medical advice.

Questionnaire: series of questions to be answered truthfully on a piece of paper or online.

Food diary: a daily log of food and drink intake.

Read about it

Read about PAR- Q and try the test for yourself:
www.tinyurl.com/y8e7geo4
OR
www.tinyurl.com/y8e7geo4

	Question	Yes	No
1	Do you have a bone or joint problem which could be made worse by exercise?	☐	☐
2	Has your doctor ever said that you have a heart condition?	☐	☐
3	Do you experience chest pains on physical exertion?	☐	☐
4	Do you experience light-headedness or dizziness on exertion?	☐	☐
5	Do you experience shortness of breath on light exertion?	☐	☐
6	Has your doctor ever said that you have a raised cholesterol level?	☐	☐
7	Are you currently taking any prescription medication?	☐	☐
8	Is there a history of coronary heart disease in your family?	☐	☐
9	Do you smoke, and if so, how many?	☐	☐
10	Do you drink more than 14 units of alcohol a week?	☐	☐
11	Are you diabetic?	☐	☐
12	Do you take physical activity less than three times a week?	☐	☐
13	Are you pregnant?	☐	☐
14	Are you asthmatic?	☐	☐
15	Do you know of any other reason why you should not exercise?	☐	☐

If you have answered yes to any questions please give more details:

_____

_____

_____

If you have answered yes to one or more questions you will have to consult with your doctor before taking part in a programme of physical exercise.

If you have answered no to all questions you are ready to start a suitable exercise programme.

I have read, understood and answered all questions honestly and confirm that I am willing to engage in a programme of exercise that has been prescribed to me.

Name _____   **Signature** _____

Instructor's name _____   **Instructor's signature** _____

Date _____

Figure 2.24 The PAR-Q questionnaire

Figure 2.25 PAR-Q and lifestyle questionnaires require the person completing it to tell the truth.

Lifestyle questionnaire

A lifestyle questionnaire is designed to help your healthcare or physical-exercise expert understand your lifestyle and thus improve your health or exercise regime. Participants are expected to answer all the questions without thinking too much about them. This is because it is generally believed that the first response is often the most accurate response. The lifestyle questionnaire is collected for analysis. Sometimes the lifestyle questionnaire also includes the same questions as the PAR-Q questionnaire, as well as others. The questionnaire may include nutritional factors, alcohol consumption, exercise goals, etc. The analysis process allows a training expert to ascertain if a person can take part in physical activity and to what extent. The decision will be based on the details the participant provides. A detailed example of a lifestyle questionnaire is available at: www.tinyurl.com/y7ybar7o

Food diary

A food diary is a common tool used by medical experts and physical trainers to help someone achieve their goals. It is often used to improve health, but can also be used to lose weight or to eat appropriately during a physical exercise regime. For example, people who take part in endurance events often need to increase carbohydrate intake. Food diaries can be self-analysed or can be evaluated by a nutritionist who then provides advice on how to adopt healthier eating habits.

If diet needs to be altered to work towards a goal it can be easily tracked in a food diary.

Client progress review

Sitting down with a client and reviewing how they are doing is a simple and effective way of helping someone evaluate their progress and focus on their goals. This is often conducted as an interview, looking at the goals set and re-evaluating whether changes need to be made.

 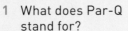

Figure 2.26 Food diaries often involve recording how much was eaten, what kind of food, when, where, who with, what you were doing at the time and the mood you were in.

3.1.2 Goal setting

When setting a goal for someone to achieve, the acronym SMART should be used.

Figure 2.27 A physical trainer re-evaluating goals with a client

SMART stands for:

- **S**pecific – specific to the demands of the sport/muscles used/ movements involved/goal to be achieved.
- **M**easurable – it must be possible to measure whether the goal has been met.
- **A**chievable – it must actually be possible to achieve/there is a way that it could be achieved
- **R**ealistic – it must actually be possible to complete the goal within a person's physical capabilities.
- **T**ime-bound – it must be set over a fixed period of time. This could be a short-term period (for example, from one day to one month) or a medium-term goal (for example, between one and six months). Anything longer than six months would be considered a long-term goal.

There are advantages and disadvantages to using SMART goals, as shown in this table.

Table 2.24 Advantages and disadvantages of using SMART goals

	Advantage	Disadvantage
Specific	Individuals within a team will know their goal and will have specific requirements/targets to aim for.	The SMART target can lead to too much focus being placed on reaching the goal.
Measurable	It is easy to monitor progress as it can be measured.	It can limit creativity if there is too much measuring.
Achievable	The performer believes that there is a way it can be reached.	It is a subjective judgement, and the performer may not believe it is achievable.
Realistic	As it is realistic, the individual has a high chance of seeing improvement as their ability is clearly there. It may make them become more motivated.	Although they may be physically capable, this will not be enough without suitable motivation and time.
Time-bound	The set time allows the performer to see the improvement and prepare punctually for an event/season.	There may be excessive pressure to meet the deadline.

Tables 2.25 and 2.26 show two examples of SMART targets in action for a goal:

Table 2.25 SMART targets for 'I will walk for 30 minutes each day of the week.'

S	specific movement (i.e. walking)
M	easy to measure (30 minutes)
A	achievable for most people
R	realistic, in that most people have the physical ability to do this
T	every day this can be checked

Table 2.26 SMART targets for 'I will lose two stone by Christmas.'

S	specific target to achieve relating to weight
M	easy to measure weight on scales
A	achievable for most people as long as it is not too near to Christmas
R	realistic, in that most people have the physical ability to lose weight by changing their consumption habits
T	by Christmas

Figure 2.28 Goals should be SMART

Test yourself

1 What does SMART stand for?
2 What is an advantage of a goal being measurable?
3 Suggest a suitable SMART goal for a person who lives a sedentary lifestyle?

Read about it

Read about example uses of SMART: **www.tinyurl.com/ybznh43b**

Remember

- A PAR-Q questionnaire is used to determine if someone can take part in physical activity or whether (on medical grounds) it is not advisable.
- Questionnaires like a lifestyle questionnaire require participants to give their first answer, as this is normally the truth.
- Food diaries often involve how much was eaten, what kind of food, when, where, who with, what people were doing at the time and the mood they were in.
- Client progress reviews allow personal trainers and clients to monitor progress and re-evaluate goals set.
- Goals set should be SMART – specific, measurable, achievable, realistic, time-bound.
- SMART goals should be realistic, in that the person must have the physical attributes to achieve such a goal.
- Time-bound goals allow a person to know when the goal should be achieved by.

Review questions

1 Describe how to collect, use, analyse and evaluate PAR-Q data.
2 Explain what is meant by a SMART goal.
3 What information does a food diary usually contain?
4 How is a client progress review usually conducted?
5 State one advantage for each of the components of a SMART target.

Learning outcome 4: understand the structure of a health and fitness programme and how to prepare safely

In this learning outcome you will develop understanding of:

- how to structure a health and fitness programme, including:
  - information that should be included in a health and fitness programme
  - information that should be included in session cards
- the purpose and importance of a warm up and cool down
- the components of the main activity section
- health and safety for a health and fitness programme.

4.1 The structure of a health and fitness programme

4.1.1 The health and fitness programme

It is very important that you know what information should be included in a health and fitness programme. If you were to design a programme for a client or colleague, the items shown in Figure 2.32 should be included in the overall plan.

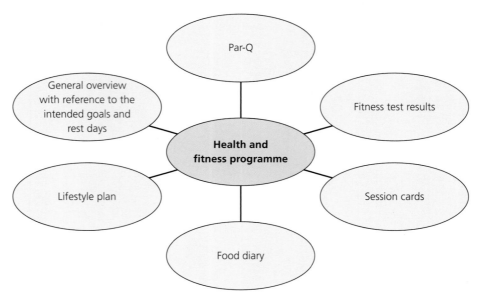

Figure 2.29 Essential components of a health and fitness programme

In designing a **health and fitness programme**, you need a definitive plan. It is easy to say 'I want to lose weight', but a key question is: how much? A general overview, making use of SMART goals, will allow the person to feel focused. If they want to lose one stone in four months, they have a specific, measurable, achievable, realistic and time-bound goal to achieve. Having a clearly stated goal or goals will help the person to remain focused and motivated. The programme itself should be balanced – considering both the amount of aerobic and anaerobic work required. Rest is essential, so the exercise plans should not be over-loaded, and recovery methods (including rest) should be scheduled in. A participant may need to do a **PAR-Q** test initially to assess their suitability for exercise before starting.

Assuming an initial PAR-Q test does not suggest that exercise is unadvisable, many health and fitness programmes will display the initial results from a bank of **fitness tests**. It is also advisable to schedule in re-tests at a point in the future so that a comparison of results can be undertaken. This will also enable the trainer and performer to monitor progress.

Having completed a **lifestyle** questionnaire, the programme itself may include some lifestyle changes. This could include sleeping patterns, aiming to get off at a bus stop earlier than usual, prioritising time to breathe slowly or meditate, etc. The programme itself may well include the use of a food diary. In doing so, the aim is that the performer eats appropriately to suitably nourish and prepare the body for the rigours of the programme.

The programme will incorporate session cards so that the person carrying out the programme knows what to do in each exercise session. Session cards are covered in detail in section 4.1.2.

Key words

Health and fitness programme: a full plan which could include the results of a PAR-Q test, lifestyle questionnaire, initial fitness-test results, a food diary and lifestyle plan, goals to be achieved and session cards to achieve the goals.

Back to fitness in 21 days!

	Monday	Tuesday	Wednesday	Thursday	Friday	Saturday	Sunday
Week 1	Walk for 3 mins and run for 1 min alternately, for a total of 20 mins	Go for a relaxed 30 min walk or a swim	Walk for 3 mins and run for 2 mins alternately, for a total of 25 mins	Go for a relaxed 30 min walk or a swim	Walk for 2 mins and run for 3 mins alternately, for a total of 25 mins	Play a sport for at least 30 mins, at the park or beach	Rest day: go to the cinema!
Week 2	Walk for 1 min and run for 4 mins alternately, for a total of 30 mins	Go for a good 45 min walk or a swim	Walk for 1 min and run for 4 mins alternately, for a total of 30 mins	Go for a good 45 min walk or a swim	Walk for 1 min and run for 5 mins alternately, for a total of 36 mins	Play a sport for at least 45 mins, at the park or beach	Rest day: treat yourself at your favourite restaurant!
Week 3	Run for 1 km and walk for 0.5 km alternately, for a total of 3 km	Go for a relaxed 60 min walk or a swim	Run for 1.5 km and walk for 0.5 km alternately, for a total of 4 km	Run for 2 km, walk for 0.5 km, then run for 1.5 km	Rest day: relax and mentally prepare for the run	Run for 3.5 km. Congrats, you did it!	Ready for a new beginning? Buy yourself a new pair of shoes!

Remember, before, during and after your workout programme:

1. Your aim is to get started on a lifetime habit of working out. So enjoy it.
2. Make your workouts a priority, as regular as your mealtimes. You won't find time for this, unless you consciously make time.
3. Don't expect every day to be the same, learn from the not-so-good days, record your good ones and stick with the programme.
4. With any fitness regime, rushing leads to injuries and discouragement. Slow and steady is the best way forward.
5. Never start or end a workout without stretching and warming up/cooling down. A brisk five-minute walk is a good way to warm up.
6. Stay hydrated.
7. Always consult with your doctor before you start any new workout routine or if you feel uneasy at any point while following a programme. Generally, your doctor will probably encourage you to begin a run–walk programme, unless you have a known health risk.

Figure 2.30 A basic 21-day programme which includes some lifestyle factors and nutritional advice as well as the exercise sessions themselves

Activity

Listen to the NHS podcasts on how to achieve their 'Couch to 5k' plan: www.tinyurl.com/ycyln72l

Test yourself

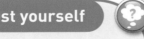

1 Why might fitness test scores be included in a health and fitness programme?
2 What is a food diary?
3 What is meant by the term 'lifestyle plan'?

Read about it

Read about designing the best session for a client: www.tinyurl.com/ycn78bh9

4.1.2 The session card

The information that is displayed in a session card is vital so that a performer knows what should be included in their training session. If it

is too vague, performers may be unsure what to do within their session. Figure 2.31 shows many of the aspects that could be included in a session card.

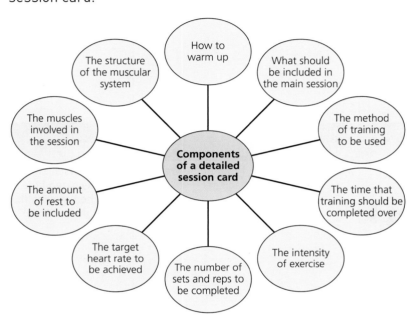

Figure 2.31 Components of a detailed session card

The session card itself may contain pictures and detailed information, but it should not be so 'wordy' that the performer finds it hard to interpret. For example, a section of the card could look something like that shown in Table 2.27.

Table 2.27 Example of a section of a session card

Warm up	Initial mobility exercises: ● finger movements ● wrist rotations ● neck turns ● ankle rotations Eight-minute pulse-raising jog on treadmill at 7 km/h Stretches – static, held for 30 seconds: major muscles in shoulders, chest, buttocks/legs Practice movements: one set of ten reps at 20 per cent of 1 rep max – shoulder press, lateral pull down, leg press			
Main session: approximately 45 minutes				
Exercise	**Muscles involved**	**Sets and reps**	**Rest**	**Information**
Bicep curl	**Biceps brachii**  **Figure 2.32**	3 sets of 15 rep's	1 minute between each set	Keep the back straight and fully extend the arm when moving the weight downwards
Tricep curl	**Triceps brachii**  **Figure 2.33**	3 sets of 15 rep's	1 minute between each set	Keep the back straight and elbow high

Day 4	Warm ups	Work sets	Rest
Incline bench dumbbell curl	1 × 12	4 × 8–12	60 sec
Lying two-arm dumbbell nose-breaker	1 × 12	4 × 8–12	60 sec
Bulgarian split squat	2 × 12	4 × 8–12	60 sec
Barbell squat or leg press	–	4 × 8–12	60 sec
Lying or seated leg curl	1 × 12	4 × 8–12	60 sec
Standing calf raise	1 × 12	3 × 8–12	60 sec
Hanging leg raise	–	3 × 15–20	30 sec
(Optional) interval training: perform any form of cardio for a total of 14 minutes	2 minute warm-up	1 minute of high intensity 1 minute of low intensity (six rounds)	

Figure 2.34 Sample session card

Read about it

Look at another example session card to increase muscle size:
www.tinyurl.com/y8kf9z7a

Activity

Try to design a basic session card for two different people:

- Person A wants to improve muscular strength in the upper and lower body.
- Person B wants to improve cardiovascular endurance over a period of a few months.

Use the intensity guidelines given in Section 2.2 Training methods (page 100).

Test yourself

1 If a participant is using weight training, what details about the weights should be included on a session card?
2 Why might a session card include pictures?
3 What kind of sets and reps would a session card contain for someone looking to develop strength?
4 What percentage of heart rate max would a session card contain for someone aiming to improve cardiovascular endurance?

4.1.3 Warm up/cool down

You need to develop knowledge of and understand the purpose and importance of a **warm up** and **cool down** and be able to apply them to a health and fitness programme.

The benefits of a warm up include:

- gradual increase in heart rate increases body temperature
- increased blood flow to the muscle
- improved range of movement and mobilisation of joints
- a gradual increase of effort to full pace
- psychological preparation to prepare for the activity
- practice of movement skills
- reduced chance of injury.

You can remember the benefits of a warm up using **TIMO**:

- **T**emperature of the body increases
- **I**njury chances reduce
- **M**ental preparation
- **O**xygen (more) supplied to working muscles.

In carrying out a warm up, there are four distinctive phases (see Table 2.28).

Table 2.28 The four phases of a warm up

1 Mobility exercises	2 Pulse-raising activity	3 Stretches	4 Practice movements
Mobility exercises during your warm up help to prepare the body for the strenuous part of the main part of your workout. These mobility exercises help to stimulate your body's main systems – e.g. the nervous system. These exercises could include: ● finger movements ● wrist rotations ● neck turns ● ankle rotations, etc.	Heart rate is gradually increased with a pulse-raising activity. This tends to be a jog, but can also include a light swim, cycle etc., which is more specific to the activity ahead. This usually lasts a few minutes.	Stretches performed can be static and/or dynamic. Static stretches stretch the major muscles to the limit for up to 30 seconds. Dynamic stretches are 'moving stretches' that slowly stretch the muscle through a movement – e.g. lunges.	Practice movements refer to activity-specific movements. This could include passing and receiving drills in netball, shooting drills in football, etc.

You can remember that a warm up has four components by using **MASH**:

- **M**obility exercises
- **A**ctivity to raise heart rate
- **S**tretching
- **H**igher-intensity and activity-specific movements.

A cool down allows the body to gradually decrease physiological responses and remove waste products. A cool down tends to involve:

- maintaining the heart rate before gradually decreasing intensity – such as a jog that slowly decreases down to walking speed
- stretching exercises to help remove waste products from the muscles.

The benefits of a cool down include:

- allowing the body to slowly reduce breathing rate to normal
- allowing the body to slowly reduce heart rate to normal
- removal of lactic acid, carbon dioxide and waste products
- prevention of delayed onset of muscle soreness/DOMS.

Figure 2.35 Stretching forms a vital part of a warm up and a cool down.

Figure 2.36 Some form of pulse-raising activity is an essential part of a warm up.

Activity

Design a suitable warm up and cool down for one of the following activities:

- continuous training at 60–80 per cent of MHR
- a weight training session for muscular endurance
- a football-specific training session.

Test yourself

1 Name three physiological benefits of warming up.
2 DOMS is the:
   a delayed oxygen to muscle site
   b delayed onset of my soreness
   c delayed oxygen to myoglobin site
   d delayed onset of muscle soreness.
3 Name three benefits of a suitable cool down.
4 State two potential negative effects of not suitably cooling down.

Read about it

Read about why we warm up and cool down: **www.tinyurl.com/yan4oro7**

4.1.4 Main activity section

You need to have knowledge of and understanding about the components of the main activity section. Different methods of training are included in the main activity section in order to meet the goals which have been set. However, the principles of training and the principles of FITT should be applied in all cases (see Unit 1, Section 4.1 Principles of training).

A training session itself will start with a warm up (see previous section, Section 4.1.3) but the choice of training type is of vital importance. Table 2.29 gives an indication of why different training may be used and potentially combined to form cross training.

Table 2.29 Variations of training in a main activity section

SMART goal	Training type/activity detail	Reason	Example application of the principles of training SPORT and FITT
To run a 10 k in six months' time	Continuous training – a starting run of 20 minutes working at 60–80% of MHR	10 k is a long-endurance event, during which the intensity will not change much. Thus, continuous training matches the aim.	**S**pecificity – running is specific to 10 k **P**rogressive – change intensity when it becomes too easy **O**verload – 60–80% of MHR is working harder than normal **R**eversibility – continue training for the whole six months **T**edium – choose different routes to run **F**requency – 2–3 times per week **I**ntensity – 60–80% of MHR **T**ime – start with 20 minutes and progress **T**ype – continuous
To lose two stone by Christmas	Cross training ● Continuous training – 20-minute jog at 60–80% of MHR ● Core training – 3 × 50 crunches with 1-minute rest between sets ● Interval training – four stations: 　1 burpees 　2 press-ups 　3 10 m shuttle runs 　4 kettle bell raises 　(initial 1:1 work to rest ratio at 60% effort for 1 minute)	A mix of training to strengthen the core muscles to help the person carry out the other types of training. Low-intensity fat burning work	**S**pecificity – specific to the goal **P**rogressive – progress intensity when it proves too easy **O**verload – working harder than normal **R**eversibility – continue training for the whole year up until Christmas **T**edium – different training types prevents boredom **F**requency – 3 times per week **I**ntensity – Continuous at 60–80% of MHR. Interval at initial 1:1 work to rest ratio **T**ime – start with 20-minute sessions **T**ype – cross

SMART goal	Training type/activity detail	Reason	Example application of the principles of training and FITT

To beat my personal best for the 100 m by the end of the season	Cross training
	● Interval training – 6 × 60 m sprints at 90% intensity with 1 minute 30 seconds rest
	● Weight training – 2–4 reps for 2–4 sets (heavy weights) at 90% of 1 rep max, to include
	   • leg press
	   • leg curl
	   • barbell ankle raises
	   • squats with dumbbells
		Event is sprint based, which requires speed and power. Speed can be developed in the interval training, and power through weight training.	**S**pecificity – specific movements and energy used for sprinting
			Progressive – intensity will be increased when it gets harder
			Overload – working harder than normal
			Reversibility – continue training until the end of the season
			Tedium – cross training provides variety
			Frequency – 3–4 times per week
			Intensity – 2–4 reps for 2–4 sets (heavy weights)
			Time – 1-hour sessions
			Type – cross

To increase my 1 rep max score for bench press and arm curl within one month	Weight training – 5–8 reps for 2–6 sets (heavy weights) at 70% of 1 rep max, to include: ● triceps curls ● bicep curls ● shoulder press ● leg press ● leg curl ● lateral pull down ● bench press	The 1 rep max score is a measure of strength, and weight training is the most effective way to increase strength.	**S**pecificity – specific muscles can be trained in the gym **P**rogressive – intensity will be increased when training is too easy **O**verload – working harder than normal **R**eversibility – keep training for the whole month **T**edium – different weights and machines can be used to prevent boredom **F**requency – 3 times per week **I**ntensity – 5–8 reps for 2–6 sets (heavy weights) **T**ime – 1-hour sessions **T**ype – weight training

Figure 2.37 Weights can be used to develop power, strength or muscular endurance.

Figure 2.38 Running is an effective way to improve cardiovascular endurance when working at 60–80% or MHR.

Read about it

Read about the reasons to choose a specific training type:

www.tinyurl.com/6l35zj

www.tinyurl.com/y87vkrk6

Activity

Choose a SMART fitness goal and produce a PowerPoint presentation which justifies the choice of training type/s you would use to meet this goal.

Test yourself

Copy this table and draw lines between the fitness aim and relevant training type. You can link a fitness aim to more than one training type.

Fitness aim	Training type
Lose weight	Continuous training
Gain muscle mass	Fartlek training
Improve netball performance	Weight training
Train for a marathon	Interval training
Change body shape to mesomorph	Circuit training
Improve cardiovascular endurance	Resistance training (using body)
Tone body muscles to show more definition	Cross training

4.1.5 Health and safety

Health and safety is always important when designing and carrying out a training programme. The person designing the session should think about:

- the environment in which the activity is taking place
- the equipment being used, checking it is safe
- clothing and footwear which is appropriate to the activity being undertaken.

Risk assessment

A risk assessment is generally carried out to assess the environment in which training is taking place. The risks are scored in relation to how bad they are, and the risk assessment highlights what needs to be done to reduce the risk. For example, in a weights gym, you would check that the weights are clean and that machines are functioning properly. When going for a run outside, suitable shoes should be worn and a safe running route selected. The general headings for a pre-activity risk assessment form are shown below.

Table 2.30 Example of headings used in a risk assessment form

WHAT ARE THE HAZARDS WHICH MAY CAUSE:	Who/what may be harmed? (give specific groups of people – e.g. staff, visitors, contractors, pupils, residents, cleaners, disabled, etc. and estimate numbers; include significant property damage)	What is done now? (i.e. provision of training, corporate and local standards complied with, existing codes of safe working practice, protective equipment, guarding, supervision, monitoring systems, specific assessments under health and safety regulations – e.g. COSHH, DSE, noise manual handling, fire, etc.)	How bad is the risk? (It may help to use the risk-assessment scoring system. Evaluate the risk as LOW, MEDIUM or HIGH.)	What needs to be done? (What action should be taken or needs to be considered in order that the risks identified are effectively controlled?)	By when? (What is the target date for completion?)

Source: Bracknell Leisure Centre

One particular way to prevent injury is to ensure that the training type and intensity used matches the training purpose. For example, a marathon runner would not use heavy weights and would not perform a great deal of anaerobic work.

Some simple points relating to health and safety are given below. All training types require most of these.

- A warm up should be completed before every type of training.
- Overtraining should be avoided.

- An appropriate weight should be chosen to lift when resistance training.
- Appropriate clothing and footwear should be worn (for example, shoes should be tied, use running shoes for running, wear clothing that is not too baggy for weight training, etc.).
- Hydration should be maintained.
- Any 'weak areas' should be taped or braced to prevent injury.
- Heavy weights may require a 'spotter'.
- Stretches should not be bounced or overstretched.
- Technique should be correct when lifting weights or resistance.
- Rest periods should be regular and planned.

Figure 2.39 Running shoes should fit appropriately and provide a range of movement, support and protection for the feet.

Figure 2.40 Heavy weights may require a 'spotter' to give support when lifting the weight.

Activity

Before training, write down what points you should consider to prevent injury from occurring.

Design a risk assessment of one of the recreational areas of your school/college.

Test yourself

1 State two safety factors to consider in order to prevent injury before a session of long-distance continuous running.

2 Describe three factors to consider to prevent injury before starting a weight training session.

3 Why should you score a risk as high, medium or low?

Remember

- A general training programme should include:
  - general overview with reference to the intended goals and rest days
  - lifestyle plan
  - food diary
  - Par-Q
  - fitness test results
  - session cards.
- Fitness test results are often displayed so that improvement can be monitored after training.
- Weight training sessions include details regarding the number of sets and reps.
- A warm up holds benefits, such as gradually increasing temperature, heart rate and breathing rate.
- A cool down holds many benefits, such as gradually reducing heart rate and removing waste products.
- Continuous training is generally chosen as a training method to improve cardiovascular endurance.
- Weight training is generally chosen to improve strength, power or muscular endurance.
- A risk assessment is generally carried out before training starts to assess the risks and plan to reduce the chance of them occurring.
- Before working out in a gym, the instructor tends to check that the weights are clean and machines are functioning correctly.

Review questions

1. State three things that could be included in a session card.
2. Describe the four main components of a warm up.
3. State three benefits of warming up.
4. Give three examples of common mobility exercises included in a warm up.
5. Give two benefits of cooling down after training.
6. Suggest five factors to consider to prevent injury when weight training.
7. Once a risk is identified, what three things need to be considered as part of the risk assessment?
8. What can weight training be used to improve?

Glossary

1 rep max: the maximum weight that can be lifted in one repetition.

Abduction: movement where a part of the body is taken away from the midline of the body, for example, moving the legs apart.

Active lifestyle: a lifestyle in which the person chooses to include suitable levels of exercise.

Adduction: movement where a part of the body is brought towards the midline of the body, for example, bringing the arms into the sides.

Aerobic energy system: uses/is dependent on oxygen; used for long-duration, low-intensity activities.

Aerobic training zone: working at 60–80 per cent of maximal heart rate.

Agility: the ability to move and change direction quickly (at speed) while maintaining control.

Agonist: the contracting muscle; the muscle that causes movement.

Alveoli: minute air sacs in the lungs.

Anaerobic energy system: not dependent on oxygen and used for short duration; used for high-intensity activities.

Anaerobic training zone: anything over 80 per cent of maximal heart rate.

Antagonist: muscle that relaxes to allow the agonist to contract.

Aorta: blood vessel carrying oxygenated blood from the left ventricle to the body.

Appendicular skeleton: the outer part of the skeleton.

Artery: blood vessel carrying blood away from the heart.

Articulating cartilage: protective covering on ends of bones.

Atria: upper chambers of the heart that collect blood from veins.

Axial skeleton: the central part of the skeleton.

Balance: the maintenance of the centre of mass over the base of support.

Biceps: located on the front of the upper arm; cause flexion at the elbow.

Body composition: a comparison of the percentages of bone, fat, water and muscle within the body.

Bradycardia: lower resting heart-rate as a result of training.

Bronchi: two tubes that carry air from the trachea into each lung.

Bronchioles: tiny tubes that carry air to the alveoli.

Caliper: device used to measure skinfold to calculate body composition.

Capillary: very thin blood vessels that allow gas exchange to happen.

Cardiac output: amount of blood leaving the heart per minute.

Cardiovascular endurance: the ability of the heart and lungs to supply oxygen to the working muscles.

Cartilage: a firm connective tissue.

Cervical: neck vertebrae.

Circuit training: a series of exercises performed one after the other to complete a 'circuit', with a rest in between each circuit.

Coccyx: lowest part of spine; allows attachment of ligaments and muscles.

Concentric: isotonic contraction where the muscle shortens.

Cool down: allows a slow reduction in the heart and breathing rate to enable recovery to occur effectively.

Co-ordination: the ability to use different (two or more) parts of the body together smoothly and efficiently.

Glossary

Cross training: a term used for any exercise programme that makes use of two or more differing training types.

Deltoid: located on the shoulder; causes abduction of the arm.

Deoxygenated blood: blood returning to the heart/lungs lacking oxygen.

Diastolic pressure: the blood pressure in the arteries when the heart rests between beats.

Dietary manipulation: changing diet to improve performance or recovery.

Diffusion: movement of substances from a high concentration to a lower concentration.

DOMS: delayed onset of muscle soreness.

Dynamometer: device used to measure strength in the hand.

Eccentric: isotonic contraction where the muscle lengthens – used to control downward movements.

Ectomorph: body shape characterised by lean, skinny, low muscle mass. Ectomorphs are often tall.

Endomorph: body shape characterised by large fat content.

Exhalation: breathing air out.

Fartlek: fartlek training is a Swedish name for 'speed play' whereby the work rate intensity and terrain change from high to lower and back to higher.

Fitness: the ability to cope with daily demands without suffering undue fatigue. In other words, your body is fit enough to do what it needs to do.

Flexibility: the range of movement possible at a joint.

Food diary: a daily log of food and drink intake.

Frequency: increase how often you train for.

Gastrocnemius: located on the back of the lower legs; causes straightening of the ankle.

Gluteus maximus: located on the buttocks; causes extension of the hips.

Gravity: the natural pull towards the earth's core.

Hamstrings: located on the back of the upper leg; cause flexion at the knee.

Health: a state of complete physical, mental and social wellbeing and not merely the absence of disease or infirmity (WHO, 1948).

Health and fitness programme: a full plan which could include the results of a PAR-Q test, lifestyle questionnaire, initial fitness-test results, a food diary and lifestyle plan, goals to be achieved and session cards to achieve the goals.

Heart rate: the number of times the heart beats in a minute.

High blood pressure: blood pressure above 120/80.

Hip flexors: located on the front of the upper legs; cause flexion of the legs.

Hypertrophy: increase in size due to training (e.g. hypertrophy of the left ventricle in the heart).

Inspiration: breathing air in.

Intensity: increase how much training is done.

Interval training: any type of training that involves altering periods of work with periods of rest.

Involuntary muscle: muscle that we have no control over.

Isometric: muscle action where the muscle stays the same length – used in balances.

Isotonic: muscle action where the muscle changes length – causes movement.

Joint: where two or more bones meet.

Joint capsule: holds bones in place.

Kettle bell: a type of free weight.

Kilocalorie (kcal): calorie is the term used to represent one unit of food energy.

Kyphosis: excessive outward curve of thoracic region of the spine.

Lactic acid: fatiguing waste product of the anaerobic energy system.

Larynx: voice box.

Latissimus dorsi: located on the back; causes adduction of the arm.

Left atrium: heart chamber receiving deoxygenated blood from the vena cava.

Left ventricle: heart chamber pumping oxygenated blood into the aorta.

Lifestyle: refers to the choices we make about how we live our lives.

Ligaments: joins bones to bone; supports and reinforces joint capsule.

Lordosis: excessive inward curve of lumbar region of the spine.

Low blood pressure: blood pressure less than 90/60.

Lumbar: lower back vertebrae; weight-bearing.

Massage: involves rubbing and 'kneading' of the muscles, which helps to reduce pain and encourages blood flow through the muscles.

Maximal: working with 100 per cent effort.

Maximum heart rate (MHR): calculated as 220 – age.

Mesomorph: body shape characterised by large muscular shoulders.

Minerals: substances that cannot be made by living things. Some minerals are essential for the human body.

Mouth and nose: air enters the body through these.

Muscular endurance: the ability of a muscle or muscle group to undergo repeated contractions avoiding fatigue.

National average: a table of normative data that provides categorised scores for test results.

Normative data: refers to the use of national standards to show what is normal, excellent, good, average, below average or poor.

Overload: working harder than normal.

Oxygenated blood: blood leaving the heart/lungs rich in oxygen.

PAR-Q: a simple 'yes/no' questionnaire that aims to identify the small number of people for whom physical activity might be unsuitable on the grounds of medical advice.

Pectoralis major: located on the chest; causes adduction of the arm.

Performance-enhancing drugs: illegally taken drugs, taken in order to enhance performance rather than for recreational reasons.

Pharynx: chamber at the back of the throat.

Power: explosive strength or anaerobic power is the product of strength and speed: i.e. strength × speed.

Progression: gradually increasing the intensity of training.

Pulmonary artery: blood vessel carrying deoxygenated blood from the right ventricle to the lungs.

Pulmonary vein: blood vessel carrying oxygenated blood from the lungs to the left atrium.

Quadriceps: located on the front of the upper leg; cause extension at the knee.

Questionnaire: series of questions to be answered truthfully on a piece of paper or online.

Reaction time: the time taken to initiate a response to a stimulus.

Recommended daily allowance (RDA): the number of calories, or amount of nutrients that is recommended you consume on an average day. The recommended daily allowance for men is 2500 kcal per day and 2000 kcal per day for women. As a term, the recommended daily allowance also includes the recommended amount of nutrients the body needs. An average adult (19–64 years old) is recommended to:

- eat less than 70 g of fat per day
- eat less than 20 g of saturated fat per day
- eat at least 260 g of carbohydrate
- eat no more than 90 g of sugars (although no more than 30 g of 'free sugars' included in sweets, fizzy drinks, etc.)
- eat approximately 50 g of protein
- eat less than 6 g of salt.

Glossary

Recovery: what a performer does to allow repair of the body.

Recreational drugs: drugs taken for recreational purposes rather than performance-enhancing capabilities.

Rectus abdominis: located on the stomach wall; causes flexion of the trunk and hips.

Red blood cell: carries oxygen in the blood.

Reliability: a fitness test is only valid if when repeated, similar results are gained.

Rep: a single completion of one lift of the resistance being used.

Residual volume: amount of air left in the lungs after a maximal exhalation.

Rest: a time when a performer undertakes little or no exertion.

Reversibility: you lose fitness if you stop or reduce training.

Right atrium: heart chamber receiving oxygenated blood from the pulmonary vein.

Right ventricle: heart chamber pumping deoxygenated blood into the pulmonary artery.

Rotation: movement where a whole limb or part of the body turns or revolves around its length.

Sacrum: attached to pelvis.

Sedentary lifestyle: refers to a person's choice to have little or no exercise.

Set: a collection of repetitions that occur before a period of rest.

Soleus: located on the back of the lower legs; causes straightening of the ankle.

Specificity: training must be relevant for your chosen activity.

Speed: the maximum rate at which an individual is able to perform a movement or cover a distance in a period of time. It is also defined as putting the body parts into action as quickly as possible.

Station: an area where a specific exercise is repeated for a set period of time.

Steady-state exercise: working at a constant intensity.

Strength: the ability to overcome a resistance.

Striated: striped muscle.

Stroke volume: amount of blood leaving the heart each beat.

Synovial membrane: produces synovial fluid.

Synovial fluid: lubricates joint.

Systolic pressure: the blood pressure in the arteries during the contraction of your heart.

Tedium: training needs to be varied to avoid boredom.

Terrain: the surface or conditions upon which one is running.

Tendons: attach muscles to bones.

Thoracic: chest vertebrae; attached to ribs.

Tidal volume: amount of air that enters the lungs during normal inspiration at rest.

Time: increase the duration of your training.

Trachea: often called the windpipe, lined with rings of cartilage and carries air from the pharynx to the bronchi.

Trapezius: located on the neck; causes extension of the head.

Triceps: located on the back of the upper arm; cause extension at the elbow.

Type: vary the type of training.

Type 1 slow-twitch fibres: muscle fibre that is red, contracts slowly and is resistant to fatigue.

Type 2 fast-twitch fibres: muscle fibre that is white, contracts rapidly and fatigues easily.

Unstriated: unstriped muscle.

Validity: a fitness test is only valid if the score is calculated using the correct procedures.

Vascular shunt: mechanism that directs blood to where there is greater demand.

Vasoconstriction: reducing the diameter of small arteries to reduce blood flow to tissues.

Vasodilation: increasing the diameter of small arteries to increase blood flow to tissues.

Vein: blood vessel carrying blood towards the heart.

Vena cava: blood vessel carrying deoxygenated blood from the body to the right atrium.

Ventricles: lower chambers of the heart that pump blood out of the heart to the arteries.

Vital capacity: maximum amount of air you can exhale after taking the deepest possible inspiration.

Voluntary muscle: muscle that we can control.

Warm up: exercise to prepare the body for exercise so that the chances of injury or ill effects are limited.

Work: a level of exertion which is harder than normal.

Unit 1 answers

1.1 Skeletal system

1.1.1 Structure of the skeleton

1 cranium, ribs, sternum, vertebrae
2 humerus, radius, ulna, (carpals, phalanges)
3 (pelvis), femur, tibia, fibula, (tarsals, phalanges)
4 carpals, phalanges, tarsals, phalanges

1.1.2 Functions of the skeletal system

1 support, movement, protection, storage of minerals, blood cell production, shape
2 red blood cells
3 cranium, ribs
4 calcium, phosphorus

1.1.3 Types of bones

1 long, flat, short, irregular
2 femur/tibia/humerus
3 support and stability
4 sternum, scapula, ribs

1.1.4 Types of joints

1 pivot, condyloid, saddle, gliding, ball and socket, hinge
2 wrist – condyloid, clavicle – gliding
3 pivot – vertebrae, saddle – thumb
4 shoulder, hip
5 elbow, knee

1.1.5 Joint actions

1 flexion, extension
2 abduction – away from body, adduction towards body
3 rotating/turning leg out/in

1.1.6 Structure of a synovial joint (knee)

1 Labels should include: articular cartilage, ligaments, joint capsule, synovial membrane and synovial fluid.
2 joint capsule – holds joint in place, ligaments – join bone to bone
3 synovial membrane – produces synovial fluid, synovial fluid – lubricates joint
4 articulating cartilage – protective covering of ends of bone/absorbs shocks
5 quadriceps – cause extension at knee, hamstrings – cause flexion at knee

1.1.7 Structure of the spine and posture

1 Labels should include: cervical, thoracic, lumbar vertebrae, sacrum and coccyx.
2 cervical – support weight of head, thoracic – hold ribs in place and protect heart, lumbar – support weight of body, sacrum – connect spine to pelvis, coccyx – attachment for ligaments and muscles
3 reduces stress on muscles, ligaments and tendons
4 muscles and ligaments are unable to work properly, too much stress is placed on certain muscles
5 lordosis – inward curve of lumbar spine, kyphosis – outward curve of lumbar spine

Review questions

1 femur, tibia, carpals
2 clavicle, scapula, phalanges
3 radius and ulna, tibia and fibula
4 calcium, phosphorus
5 red blood cells, white blood cells
6 for example, rugby, football, karate (and many others)
7 for example, femur, clavicle, vertebrae, pelvis

8 long, irregular, short

9 used for movement; red blood-cell production

10 support; stability

11 for example, cranium, pelvis, vertebrae, ribs, sternum

12 hinge, condyloid

13 pelvis and femur, scapula and humerus

14 flexion and extension

15 condyloid (wrist), saddle (thumb), hinge (elbow/knee), ball and socket (hip/shoulder)

16 extension

17 flexion

18 abduction and adduction

19 adduction and abduction

20 flexion, extension, adduction, abduction, rotation

21 ligaments – join bone to bone, tendons – attach muscles to bone

22 function – lubrication/reduce friction, it's produced by synovial membrane

23 fibrous capsule, ligaments

24 hamstring

25 cervical – support; thoracic – protection; lumbar – weight-bearing; sacral – joins spine to pelvis

26 sacral vertebrae and coccyx

27 It reduces stress on ligaments, tendons and muscles; allows muscles to work efficiently; decreases wear and tear on joints so reducing risk of joint discomfort and injuries.

28 Lordosis is excessive inward curve of the lumbar region of the spine. Kyphosis is excessive outward curve of thoracic region of the spine.

1.2 Muscular system

1.2.1 Types of muscle

1 cardiac, smooth and skeletal

2 cardiac – heart; smooth – digestive tract and blood vessels; skeletal – muscles around body

3 involuntary, fatigue resistant, oxygen dependent

4 not oxygen dependent, involuntary

5 not oxygen dependent, voluntary

6 aids blood flow through heart

7 aids digestion and distribution of blood

8 aids movement

1.2.2 Structure of the muscular system

1 knee flexion – hamstrings, knee extension – quadriceps; elbow flexion – biceps, elbow extension – triceps

2 deltoid – abduction of arm, latissimus dorsi – adduction of arm, pectoralis major – adduction of arm, trapezius – extension of head

3 rectus abdominus – flexion of trunk and hips, gluteus maximus – extension at hips, hip flexors – flexion at hip

4 gastrocnemius – straightening of ankle (plantar flexion), soleus – straightening of ankle (plantar flexion)

1.2.3 Muscle movement and contraction

1 knee flexion – agonist = hamstrings, antagonist = quadriceps; elbow flexion – agonist = biceps, antagonist = triceps

2 isotonic – movement occurs; isometric – no movement

3 concentric – muscle shortens; eccentric – muscle lengthens

1.2.4 Muscle fibre types

1 type 1 slow-twitch, type 2 fast-twitch

2 type 1 slow-twitch – red, contracts slowly, fatigue resistant; type 2 fast-twitch – white, contracts rapidly, fatigues easily

3 long, slow activities – walking, jogging, slow cycling and swimming

4 fast, strenuous activities – sprinting, jumping, tackling

Review questions

1 It contracts to assist movement and still returns to its original shape. It is voluntary, and striped/striated.

2 walls of organs (for example, digestive tract and lungs), walls of blood vessels

3   It contracts when the heart beats. It is involuntary and very resistant to fatigue.

4   smooth muscle, cardiac muscle

5   cardiac muscle, skeletal muscle

6   hip – gluteals, knee – quadriceps, ankle – gastrocnemius

7   pectorals, latissimus dorsi

8   extension of the skull

9   hip flexors – flexion of hip; rectus abdominus – flexion of trunk

10   hip – gluteals and eccentric, knee – quadriceps and eccentric

11   abduction – deltoid and concentric, adduction – deltoid and eccentric

12   In the held position the arms are straight – isometric, the downwards movement involves eccentric contraction of the triceps, and the upwards movement involves concentric contraction of the triceps.

13   The event demands long duration and slow contractions, and runners need to resist fatigue – this requires type 1 slow-twitch characteristics.

14   Type 2 fast-twitch fibres are used in this short distance/duration event, in which there is a need for fast, powerful contractions for speed.

15   There will be parts of the activity where there is a need for fast powerful contractions, such as jumping to head a ball – this is suited to type 2 fast-twitch fibres. At other times, during matches lasting 90 minutes, there will be resting, walking and jogging, which require slow contractions – type 1 slow-twitch fibres.

1.3 Respiratory system

1.3.1 Structure of the respiratory system

1   (nose) pharynx, larynx, trachea, bronchi, bronchioles, alveoli

2   Bronchioles are minute tubes; at the end on each bronchiole are several alveoli, like a small bunch of grapes.

1.3.2 Functions of the respiratory system

1   diaphragm and intercostals

2   The diaphragm becomes dome-shaped, ribs are lifted upwards, and the chest cavity increases in volume.

3   It is the movement of substances/gases from an area of high concentration to an area of lower concentration.

4   moist, thin walls, a large surface area, a short diffusion distance, alveoli are surrounded by capillaries

1.3.3 Lung volumes

1   tidal volume – amount of air moving in or out of the lungs during normal breathing/at rest, residual volume – amount of air left in lungs after maximal exhalation, vital capacity – maximum amount of air that can be exhaled after a maximum inspiration

2   Men and women have similar tidal volumes. Men have a larger vital capacity (4.8 litres versus 3.1 litres) and a larger residual volume (1.2 litres versus 1.1 litres).

Review questions

1   trachea, bronchi, (lungs), bronchioles, alveoli

2   diaphragm, intercostals

3   The breathing muscles (diaphragm and intercostals) relax. The diaphragm returns to its dome shape and the weight of the ribs causes them to descend. Chest volume decreases, which increases the pressure of air in the lungs, so the air is expelled (this is a passive process).

4   three of: thin membranes, layer of moisture, large surface area, short diffusion pathway, rich blood supply

5   Oxygen diffuses from high concentration in alveoli to a lower concentration in the blood. Carbon dioxide diffuses from high concentration in blood to a lower concentration in alveoli.

6   residual volume

7   vital capacity

8   tidal volume

1.4 Cardiovascular system

1.4.1 Structure and function of the blood vessels

1 Arteries have thick muscular walls. Veins have thin walls with valves. Capillaries have very thin walls.

2 Arteries carry oxygenated blood away from the heart under pressure. Veins carry deoxygenated blood towards the heart under low pressure. Capillaries assist with gaseous exchange at the lungs.

3 vasoconstriction – narrowing of arteries, vasodilation – widening of arteries

4 In order to move blood to where it is needed most from areas where demand is less.

1.4.2 Structure of the heart

1 right atrium, left atrium, right ventricle, left ventricle

2 right atrium – vena cava, left atrium – pulmonary vein, right ventricle – pulmonary artery, left ventricle – aorta

3 left side

1.4.3 The cardiac cycle

1 vena cava – right atrium – right ventricle – pulmonary artery – lungs

2 lungs – pulmonary veins – left atrium – left ventricle – aorta

1.4.4 Cardiovascular measurements

1 max HR = 220 – age

2 cardiac output – volume/amount of blood leaving the heart per minute, stroke volume – volume/amount of blood leaving the heart per beat

3 cardiac output = stroke volume × heart rate

4 Systolic pressure is the pressure in the arteries during contraction of the heart. Diastolic pressure is the pressure in the arteries during relaxation of the heart.

5 systolic – 90–120 mmHg, diastolic – 60–80 mmHg

6 for example: high blood pressure – 140/90 mmHg, low blood pressure – 90/60 mmHg

Review questions

1 Arteries have a thicker wall, no valves and smaller lumen than veins.

2 Arteries carry (mainly) oxygenated blood. They carry blood away from the heart, and they have a pulse.

3 They enable gaseous exchange at the lungs and at tissues (muscles), and the diffusion of nutrients and waste products.

4 Vasoconstriction is the reduction in size of blood vessels/volume of blood flow. Vasodilation is the increase in size of blood vessels/volume of blood flow.

5 right atrium

6 left ventricle

7 vena cava to the heart, pulmonary artery away from the heart

8 pulmonary vein to the heart, aorta away from the heart

9 It enters the right atrium, then travels to the right ventricle, then through the pulmonary artery to the lungs, where it becomes oxygenated.

10 It enters the left atrium, then travels to the left ventricle, then out of the heart in the aorta.

11 max HR = 220 – age, so the MHR = 220 – 24 = 196

12 Cardiac output is the volume of blood that the heart is able to pump out in one minute. Stroke volume is the volume of blood that leaves the heart during each contraction.

cardiac output (CO) = stroke volume (SV) × heart rate (HR)

13 between 120/80 mmHg (systolic) and 90/60 mmHg (diastolic)

1.5 Energy systems

1 glucose + oxygen → energy + carbon dioxide + water

2 glucose → energy + lactic acid

3 Lactic acid causes fatigue.

4 aerobic – resting, walking, jogging; anaerobic – sprinting, jumping, tackling

Review questions

1 glucose + oxygen → energy + carbon dioxide + water

2 Two of: Aerobic energy uses oxygen; in anaerobic energy no oxygen is used. Aerobic energy is used in long-duration activity; anaerobic energy is used in short-duration activity. Aerobic energy is used in low-intensity activities; anaerobic energy is used in high-intensity activities.

3 For example, football, resting, walking, jogging are aerobic; sprinting, tackling, heading are anaerobic

2.1 Effects of health and fitness activities on the body

2.1.1 Short-term effects of health and fitness activities

1 Answers include: get hot and sweaty, get red skin as the blood is shunted towards the surface, have an increase in the depth and frequency of breathing, have an increase in heart rate

2 feeling tired/fatigued, feeling light headed (particularly if dehydration has occurred)

3 Exercise will make them hot, therefore skin goes red. Muscle tears occur and lactic acid builds up.

2.1.2 Long-term effects of health and fitness activities

1 body shape may change (e.g. more muscle tone), improvements in specific components of fitness (cardiovascular endurance), improved muscular endurance, improved stamina (being able to withstand fatigue), increase in the size of the heart (hypertrophy), lower resting heart rate (bradycardia)

2 body shape may change (e.g. more muscle tone), improvements in specific components of fitness (muscular endurance), slight increase in the size of the heart (hypertrophy), slightly lower resting heart rate (bradycardia)

3 by stretching

Review questions

1 heart rate increases, breathing rate quickens and deepens

2 muscular shoulders, large muscle bulk, wedge-shaped body, narrow hips

3 Any three from: body shape may change (e.g. more muscle tone), improvements in specific components of fitness (cardiovascular endurance), improved muscular endurance, improved stamina (being able to withstand fatigue), increase in the size of the heart (hypertrophy), lower blood pressure (as exercise increases the size of your heart, more blood can be pumped out per beat), lower resting heart rate (bradycardia), improved ability to use oxygen, more red blood cells produced

4 get hot and sweaty, get red skin as the blood is shunted towards the surface, have an increase in the depth and frequency of breathing, experience an increase in heart rate

5 As heart rate and stroke volume increase during exercise, so does cardiac output.

6 The amount of blood ejected from the heart ventricles per beat (contraction)

7 The volume of blood pumped out by the heart per minute. It is calculated as stroke volume (SV) × heart rate (HR).

8 Delayed onset of muscle soreness – it occurs as a short-term effect after exercise

9 Lower resting heart rate (below 60 bpm) – this happens due to prolonged training (usually endurance-based training)

3.1 Health and fitness

1 The three components of health are: physical, mental and social.

2 Fitness and health do not necessarily relate to or guarantee each other. Being fit does not necessarily mean you are healthy – you can be physically fit but have poor social health, for example. Poor health can result in an inability to train, which would lower fitness.

Poor mental health may result in an obsessive desire to train and can lead to higher levels of fitness. It is possible to be unhealthy but able to train, and therefore increase fitness.

3 Fitness and health do not necessarily relate to or guarantee each other. Being fit does not necessarily mean you are healthy – you can be physically fit but have poor social health, for example. The chances are that training will improve your physical health, and it may also improve your social and mental health. It is possible to be unhealthy but able to train, and therefore increase fitness.

3.2 Components of fitness

3.2.1 Health-related fitness

1 Cardiovascular endurance is the ability of the heart and lungs to provide oxygen to the working muscles.

2 Flexibility is needed in gymnastics in order to perform the splits. Static strength is needed in gymnastics to hold a handstand.

3 agility, strength and muscular endurance

3.2.2 Skill-related fitness

1 Agility is 'the ability to move and change direction quickly (at speed) while maintaining control'.

2 Speed is needed in netball to intercept the ball or an opposition's pass, and to run into space away from a marker.

3 An example of stimulus and response needing reaction time is the 100 m, where a starting gun is the stimulus and the start of running is the response.

4 hands and eyes

Review questions

1 a state of complete physical, mental and social wellbeing and not merely the absence of disease or infirmity

2 power, co-ordination, reaction time, agility, balance, speed

3 Two from: power (to punch with force and speed), co-ordination (to co-ordinate leg movements and arm movements), reaction time (to dodge a punch), agility (to change direction at speed around the ring), balance (to stay standing when hit), speed (to move quickly in the ring)

4 to move feet and swing racket to hit a shuttlecock

5 the ability of the heart and lungs to supply oxygen to the working muscles

6 cardiovascular endurance, flexibility, muscular endurance, strength, body composition

7 a comparison of the percentages of bone, fat, water and muscle within the body

8 Either sport lasts a long time therefore the aerobic energy system is used. Oxygen has to be transported to the working muscles to allow the body to last the length of the game.

4.1 Principles of training

4.1.1 The principles of training

1 specificity, progression, overload, reversibility, tedium

2 specificity – training must be relevant to chosen activity, progression – gradually increase training as fitness improves, overload – train harder than normal, reversibility – stopping/reducing training loses fitness, tedium – vary training to avoid boredom

3 Lactic acid causes fatigue.

4 aerobic – slow, easy, lasting more than a minute, anaerobic – fast, powerful, lasting less than a minute

4.1.2 Principles of FITT

1 frequency, intensity, time, type

2 frequency – how often, intensity – how hard, time – how long, type – change/vary type of training

3 For example: football – train three times a week instead of twice (frequency), make training harder than normal (intensity), train

for 45 minutes instead of 30 minutes (time), train for fitness, on pitch, in gym, practice skills and set pieces (type)

Review questions

1 specificity, progression, overload, reversibility, tedium

2 Specificity – making training the same as the activity in terms of duration, intensity, skills, energy systems, etc.

3 Increase the intensity (how hard), frequency (how often), time (how long), and type (change activity) of training as the performer gets fitter

4 Frequency, intensity, time, type

5 Make the training harder with more exercises, less rest, longer duration, more weights, etc.

Unit 2 answers

1.1 Lifestyle factors

1.1.1 Activity levels

1 lifestyle – the choices we make about how we live our lives, active lifestyle – making choices to include exercise in our lives; sedentary lifestyle – choosing to take part in little or no exercise

2 Examples of moderate aerobic exercise include: brisk walking, hiking, pushing a lawn mower, playing team sports recreationally, skateboarding.

Examples of vigorous exercise include: swimming fast, running, martial arts, playing a team sport.

Examples of strength exercises include: lifting weights, use of resistance bands, heavy gardening, using your own body weight (e.g. sit-ups/press-ups).

1.1.2 Diet

1 They are the main source of energy at all intensities.

2 as an energy source at low intensity and for insulation

3 growth and repair

4 d – medium to high intensity activities

5 Minerals are required for bone growth and the maintenance of regular body functions.

1.1.3 Rest and recovery

1 Rest: a time when a performer undertakes little or no exertion. Recovery: what a performer does to allow repair of the body.

2 7–9 hours

3 Massage, which involves rubbing and 'kneading' of the muscles. This helps to reduce pain and encourages blood flow through the muscles, and so helps to flush out waste products.

1.1.4 Other factors

1 Two from: Smoking can irritate the respiratory system. It reduces the lungs' ability to function efficiently. It causes breathlessness. Gaseous exchange in the lungs is negatively affected – causing a person to cough.

2 Recreational drugs are drugs taken for recreational purposes rather than performance-enhancing capabilities. Performance-enhancing drugs are illegally-taken drugs used in order to enhance performance rather than for recreational reasons.

3 Most stress is bad for a person's health. It can increase blood pressure, put stress on the heart, weaken your immune system and affect hormone balance.

Review questions

1 An active lifestyle is a lifestyle in which the person chooses to include suitable levels of exercise.

2 Three from: disposable income, friends, family, culture, religion, accessibility, attitudes, time available, etc.

3 Physical health – person is awake and able to function normally. Allows the body's systems a chance to repair and rest.

Mental health – a lack of sleep can lead to worry about not sleeping and therefore a person will sleep less. They may therefore feel less confident or less able to concentrate.

4 55–60 per cent carbohydrates, 25–30 per cent fat, 15–20 per cent protein

5 A sedentary lifestyle is a lifestyle where the person has chosen to have little or no exercise.

6 An appropriate level of rest should be given to ensure the fitness aim is met, thus stressing the body's systems (including energy systems) suitably, whilst allowing time to recover for the next repetition.

7 Rest provides a chance to recover.

8 Diuretics can help athletes to lose weight (e.g. jockeys). However, this can lead to (one of): dehydration, low blood pressure and muscle cramps.

9 Recreational drugs are drugs taken for recreational purposes rather than performance-enhancing capabilities.

Performance-enhancing drugs are illegally taken drugs, used in order to enhance performance rather than for recreational reasons.

10 Stress can: increase blood pressure, put stress on the heart, weaken your immune system and affect hormone balance.

2.1 Fitness testing

2.1.1 Health-related fitness

1 multi-stage fitness test

2 Have handgrip dynamometer ready at zero. The dynamometer should be held in the participant's dominant hand. Squeeze with maximum effort. Record score on dial. Repeat x3 and record best score. Compare with national averages.

3 20 m

4 Have sit and reach box ready. Start in sitting position on the floor with legs straight. No shoes are to be worn and feet should be flat against the sit and reach board. Slider (if available) should be set to 14 cm to be in line with the toes. The individual reaches forward and pushes the slider as far as possible. Score is recorded in cm and compared with national averages

5 muscular endurance

2.1.2 Skill-related fitness

1 Start with a ball (e.g. tennis ball) in one hand. Stand 2 m from the wall (both feet need to be together). When 'go' is called the time starts (test is 30 seconds long). Throw the ball against the wall so as to catch the ball with the opposite hand. Count the number of catches. Repeat as many times as possible within the 30 seconds. Two attempts are allowed and then compare with national averages.

2 Record the time taken to run around the cones.

3 The distance jumped is measured and marked on the ruler in cm.

4 standing stork test

2.1.3 Using data

1 data that is taken from a large sample and compiled to show national averages in different categories

2 national average tables

3 Having taken a test it is normal that training is devised to aim to improve fitness. Thus, when training has taken place, the most obvious way to check improvement is by re-testing. Re-testing will determine whether training has been successful and how much improvement has taken place.

4 No – they test the fitness level

2.2, 2.3 Training methods; optimising a health and fitness programme

2.2.1, 2.3.1, 2.3.2 Training methods, heart-rate training zones, repetitions and sets

Interval training

1 the amount of work (exercise) compared with the amount of rest

2 for example: 45–60 seconds at high intensity with 30 seconds' rest

3 high-intensity interval training

Circuit training

1 an area where a specific exercise is repeated for a set period of time

2 press-ups, sit-ups, shuttle runs

3 60–80 per cent of maximal heart rate

Fartlek training

1 Fartlek training involves altering the intensity of running and the terrain.

2 because it mirrors the change in intensity that a player may experience when playing a team game (e.g. walk, jog, sprint, etc.)

3 For someone who is developing a base level of fitness, fartlek is good as it can improve both aerobic and anaerobic energy systems.

Continuous training

1 220 – age
2 60–80 per cent of maximal heart rate
3 aerobic
4 marathon running

Resistance and body weight training

1 the maximum weight you can lift once
2 12–20 reps for 2–6 sets
3 2–4 reps for 2–4 sets

Cross training

1 any exercise programme that makes use of two or more differing training types
2 continuous training for aerobic fitness, weights for strength, stretching for flexibility
3 prevents boredom, increased chance of weight loss, reduces stress on one specific body area

Review questions

1 national averages taken from a large sample of participants
2 Ensure a one-metre ruler is available. One person holds the metre ruler at zero. Participant places their thumb and index finger of their dominant hand at 50 cm (not touching the ruler). With no warning, the ruler is dropped. The participant must react to the drop by catching the ruler as fast a s possible. Score is recorded (i.e. distance from 50 cm). Three attempts are allowed and scores are compared with national averages.
3 Prepare a coned area, with cones 20 m apart. Participant runs 20 m in time with bleeps. Time between bleeps gets shorter as the level increases. Participant keeps running until they cannot keep up with the bleeps. Score is recorded as a level and bleep. Score is compared with national averages and used to predict a VO2 max score.
4 it can be re-tested and produce similar results

5 continuous training
6 two from: heavy weights can be damaging to children, incorrect technique can result in injury, heavy weights require a 'spotter'
7 power – 2–4 reps for 2–4 sets; strength – 5–8 reps for 2–6 sets; muscular endurance – 12–20 reps for 2–6 sets
8 60–80 per cent of 220 – age
9 By spreading the stress over different muscles and joints; whilst using differing movements, the body is not experiencing particular stress on one specific body part.

3.1 Health and fitness analysis and goal setting

3.1.1 Health and fitness analysis tools

1 physical-activity readiness questionnaire
2 to help their healthcare or physical exercise expert understand their lifestyle and thus improve their health or exercise regime
3 how much was eaten, what kind of food, when, where, who with, what they were doing at the time and the mood they were in

3.1.2 Goal setting

1 specific, measurable, achievable, realistic, time-bound
2 easy to monitor progress as it can be measured
3 for example: exercise twice a week for 20 minutes

Review questions

1 A questionnaire is given. A trainer/coach analyses the data and then evaluates suitability to perform physical activity.
2 specific to the demands of the sport/muscles used/movements involved/goals to be achieved, measurable (i.e. it must be possible to measure whether the goal has been met), achievable (i.e. it must actually be possible to achieve/there is a way that it could be achieved), realistic (i.e. it must actually be possible for a person to complete the goal

within their physical capabilities), time-bound (i.e. it must be set over a fixed period of time)

3 how much was eaten, what kind of food, when, where, who with, what they were doing at the time and the mood they were in

4 by interview

5 Specific – individuals within the team will know their goal and will have specific requirements/goals to aim for

Measurable – easy to monitor progress as it can be measured

Achievable – the performer believes that there is a way it can be reached

Realistic – the individual has a high chance of seeing improvement as their ability is clearly there. It may make them become more motivated

Time-bound – the set time allows the performer to see the improvement and prepare punctually for an event/season

4.1 The structure of a health and fitness programme

4.1.1 The health and fitness programme

1 to show benchmark figures to re-test in order to monitor improvements

2 a breakdown of food and liquid to be consumed to suitably nourish and/or prepare a performer for exercise

3 an overview of what choices will be made – e.g. how much sleep, how to carry out work duties, etc.

4.1.2 The session card

1 exercise, sets, reps, pictures of exercise
2 to show the participant how to do the exercise
3 5–8 reps for 2–6 sets
4 60–80 per cent of 1 rep max

4.1.3 Warm up/cool down

1 temperature increase, increase in heart rate, increase in breathing rate

2 d

3 gradual reduction in temperature and heart rate, and removal of waste products

4 may suffer from DOMS, and lactic acid might not be removed as quickly

4.1.4 Main activity section

Lose weight – continuous training

Gain muscle mass – weight training

Improve netball performance – continuous or interval or weight training, or fartlek or circuits or cross training

Train for a marathon – continuous training

Change body shape to mesomorph – weight training or circuits

Improve cardiovascular performance – continuous or fartlek

Tone body muscles to show more definition – weight training or circuits

4.1.5 Health and safety

1 type of running shoes and route to be taken

2 risk assessment; are weights/machines clean? are weights/machines functioning well?

3 so you know how much you should prioritise the actions you take to prevent the risk

Review questions

1 any three from:
- how to warm up
- what should be included in the main session
- the method of training to be used
- the time that training should be completed over
- the intensity of exercise
- the number of sets and reps to be completed
- the target heart rate to be achieved
- the amount of rest to be included
- the muscles involved in the session
- the structure of the muscular system

2 mobility exercises, activity to raise heart rate, stretching, higher-intensity and activity-specific movements

3 for example: temperature of body goes up, injury chances reduce, mental preparation, increased oxygen to the working muscles

4 For example: finger movements, wrist rotations, neck turns

5 gradually reducing heart rate and removing waste products

6 for example: use of a spotter, warm up and cool down, use correct technique, lift suitable intensities of weight, taping and bracing, suitable rest and hydration

7 how bad the risk is, what needs to be done about it, when it needs to be done by

8 strength, power or muscular endurance

Index

1 rep max 85
abdominal conditioning test 91, 93
abduction 14–15
active lifestyle 76
adduction 14–15
aerobic energy system 52–4, 100, 102, 104
   see also cardiovascular endurance
aerobic exercise 53, 58–9, 76–7
aerobic training zone 100, 105
agility 67–8, 95, 96
agonist muscle 30
alcohol 87
alveoli 35, 38
anaerobic energy system 52–4, 78, 90, 101–2, 104
anaerobic power 67, 70
anaerobic training zone 100
antagonist muscle 30
aorta 44–6
appendicular skeleton 5
arteries 42–3
articulating cartilage 16
atria 44–6
axial skeleton 4–5
balance 67–8, 95, 97
balanced diet 79
ball and socket joints 12
biceps muscle 24, 26, 28, 30–1
blood
   cell production 7, 8, 59
   circulation 46
   pressure 49–50, 57
   vessels 42
body
   composition 65–6, 91, 93
   shape 59–60
   temperature 57
body-weight training see resistance training
bone marrow 7
bones 8–9
   see also skeletal system
bradycardia 59
breathing rate 57
   see also respiratory system
bronchi 35
bronchioles 35
caliper 90–1
calories 79
capillaries 42–3
carbohydrates 78–9
cardiac muscles 22
cardiac output 49–50, 57
cardiovascular
   endurance 65–6, 90, 92
   measurements 48
   system 42–6

blood vessels 42–3
   cardiac cycle 46
   heart structure 44–5
   training 59
carotid pulse 48
carpals 4, 6, 9, 11
cartilage 10
cervical vertebrae 4, 18
circuit training 102–3
clavicle 4–5, 12
client progress review 114
coccyx 4, 18
concentric action 30
condyloid joint 11
continuous training 105–6
cool down 124–5
co-ordination 67–8, 95, 97
Couch to 5k programme 77
cranium 4–5
cross training 110
curve in spine 19–20
data
   normative 98–9
   reliability 98
   test and retest 99
   validity 98
delayed onset of muscle soreness (DOMS) 57, 84
deltoid muscle 24–5
deoxygenated blood 42, 44–6
diaphragm muscle 37
diastolic pressure 49–50
diet
   balanced 79–83
   calories 79
   eating habits 83
   Eatwell Guide 80–2
   energy balance 79
   food diary 112, 114
   nutrients 78
   portion size 82
dietary manipulation 84
diffusion 38
drugs 87
dynamometer 90–1
eating habits 83
   see also diet
Eatwell Guide 80–2
eccentric action 30–1
ectomorph 59–60
elbow 12, 28
endomorph 60
endurance 60, 65–6
energy systems see aerobic energy system; anaerobic energy system
eustress 87

exercise
  aerobic 76–7
  cardiovascular training 59
  endurance training 60
  FITT principles 72
  long-term effects of 59
  measuring intensity 48–50
  mobility exercises 124
  principles of training 70–2
  rest between repetitions 85
  short-term effects of 57–8
  strength training 77
  vigorous 77
  work: rest ratio 85, 100
  see also training
exhalation 37, 40
extension 14, 28
fartlek training 104
fast-twitch muscle fibres 33
fats 78
femur 4, 6, 8
fibre 78
fibula 4, 6, 16
fitness
  21 day programme 120
  analysis tools 112–14
    see also fitness testing
  definition 63
  health-related 65–6
  programme structure 118–28
  skill-related 67–8
  see also exercise; training
fitness testing
  agility 95, 96
  balance 95, 97
  body composition 91, 93
  cardiovascular endurance 90, 92
  co-ordination 95, 97
  flexibility 91, 94
  health-related fitness 90–4
  muscular endurance 91, 93
  muscular strength 90, 93
  power 95, 97
  reaction time 95, 97
  skill-related 95–7
  speed 95, 97
  test and retest 99
fixed joints 10
flat bones 8
flexibility 65–6, 91, 94
flexion 14, 28
food diary 112, 114
food pyramid 82
free weights 107–8
gaseous exchange 38
gastrocnemius muscle 24, 26, 27
gliding joints 12
glucose 52
gluteus maximus muscle 24, 26, 27

goal setting 115–16
hamstrings muscles 17, 24, 26, 27, 28
handgrip dynamometer test 90, 93
hazards 129–30
health
  analysis tools 112–14
    definition 63–4
    see also fitness
health-related fitness 65–6, 90–4
health and safety 129–30
heart rate 48–50, 57
heart structure 44–5
high blood pressure 49–50
high-intensity interval training (HIIT) 100
hinge joint 12
hip 12
hip flexor muscles 24, 26, 27
humerus 4, 6, 8
hydration levels 57
hypertrophy 59
ice baths 84
Illinois agility test 95, 96
inspiration 37, 40
    see also exhalation
intensity 100, 102, 104–5, 107–8
intercostal muscles 37
interval training 100–1
involuntary muscle 22
irregular bones 9
ischium 4
isometric action 31
isotonic action 30
joint capsule 16
joints
  actions 14–15
  and muscles 28, 30–1
  types of 10–12
kettle bells 103, 107–8
kilocalorie (kcal) 82
    see also calories
knee 12, 16–17, 28
kyphosis 19–20
lactic acid 52–3
larynx 35
latissimus dorsi muscle 24–5
left atrium 44–6
left ventricle 44–6
lifestyle
  impact of 76–7
  questionnaire 114
ligaments 16
long bones 8
lordosis 19–20
low blood pressure 49–50
lumbar vertebrae 4, 18–20
lung volumes 40
lungs 35, 37
mandible 4
massage 84

maximal testing 90–1
maximum heart rate (MHR) 49–50
mental health 63–4
mesomorph 59–60
metacarpals 4
metatarsals 4
minerals 7, 78
mobility exercises 124
multi-stage fitness test 90, 92
muscle fatigue 57
muscle fibre types 33
    see also muscular system
muscular endurance 65–6, 91, 93
muscular movement 30–1
muscular strength 65–6, 90, 93
muscular system 22–34
national average 90–1
neck 11
normative data 98–9
nutrients 78
overload 70–1
oxygen and aerobic energy system 52–4
oxygenated blood 46
PAR-Q (physical activity readiness questionnaire) 112–13
patella 4
pectoralis major muscle 24–5
pelvis 4, 6, 10
performance-enhancing drugs (PEDs) 87
phalanges 4, 6
pharynx 35
pivot joint 11
posture 18–20
power 67–8, 95, 97
    see also anaerobic power
practice movements 124
programme structure 118–28
progression 70–1
progressive overload 71
protein 78–9
pulmonary artery 44–6
pulmonary vein 44–6
pulse rate 48
pulse-raising activity 124
quadriceps muscles 16, 24, 26, 27, 28, 30–1
radial pulse 48
radius 4, 6, 11
reaction time 67–8, 95, 97
recommended daily allowance (RDA) 82
recovery 84–5
recreational drugs 87
rectus abdominis muscle 24, 26
red blood cells 7, 8, 59
reps 107
residual volume 40
resistance training 108–9
respiratory system 35–40
    gaseous exchange 38
    lung volumes 40

rest 84–5
reversibility 71
ribs 4–5, 7, 8, 37
right atrium 44–6
right ventricle 44–6
risk assessment 129–30
rotation 14–15
ruler drop test 95, 97
sacrum 4, 18
saddle joint 11
scapula 4–5, 8, 12
sedentary lifestyle 76
session cards 121–3
sets 107
short bones 9
shoulder 12
sit and reach test 91, 94
sit-up test 91–2, 93
skeletal muscles 23–8
skeletal system
    appendicular 5
    axial 4–5
    bones 8–9
    functions of 7
    joints 10–15, 16–17
    muscles 23–8
    structure 4, 18–20
skill-related fitness testing 95–7
skinfold caliper test 91, 93
skull 10
sleep 84
slow-twitch muscle fibres 33
SMART goals 115–16
smoking 87
smooth muscle 22–3
social health 63–4
soleus muscle 24, 27
specificity 70–1
speed 67–8, 95, 97
spine and posture 18–20
spirometer 40
standing stork test 95, 97
steady-state exercise 105
sternum 4–5, 7, 8, 37
strength training 77
    see also resistance training; weight training
stress 87–8
stretches 124
striated muscle 22
stroke volume 49–50, 57
synovial fluid 16
synovial joints 10–12, 16–17
synovial membrane 16
systolic pressure 49–50
talus 4
tarsals 4, 6, 9
tedium 71
temperature, body 57

tendons 16
terrain 104
thoracic vertebrae 4, 18–20
thumbs 11
tibia 4, 6, 16
tidal volume 40
trachea 35
training
    anaerobic training zone 100
    circuit 102–3
    continuous 105–6
    cross training 110
    fartlek 104
    high-intensity interval training (HIIT) 100
    intensity 100, 102, 104–5, 107–8
    interval 100–1
    methods 100–10
    principles of 70–2
    resistance 108–9
    weight training 59, 85, 107–8
    see also exercise; fitness
trapezius muscle 24–5

triceps muscle 24, 26, 28, 30–1
type 1 slow-twitch muscle fibres 33
type 2 fast-twitch muscle fibres 33
ulna 4, 6
vascular shunt mechanism 42
vasoconstriction 42
vasodilation 42
veins 42–3
vena cava 44–6
ventricles 44–6
vertebrae 4–5, 9, 10–11
vertical jump test 95, 97
vigorous exercise 77
vital capacity 40
voluntary muscle 23
wall toss test 95, 97
warm up 124–5
water 78–9
weight training 59, 85, 107–8
wellbeing 63
work: rest ratio 85, 100
wrist 11